W9-BTC-504

# MENTAL HEALTH FOR STUDENTS

# MENTAL HEALTH FOR STUDENTS

## A Guide for Adjusting to College

*By*

**ARTHUR G. NIKELLY, Ph.D.**

*Clinical Psychologist and Assistant Professor of Health Science*

*The University of Illinois Health Service*

*Mental Health Division*

*Urbana, Illinois*

**CHARLES C THOMAS • PUBLISHER**

*Springfield • Illinois • U.S.A.*

*Published and Distributed Throughout the World by*
CHARLES C THOMAS • PUBLISHER
Bannerstone House
301-327 East Lawrence Avenue, Springfield, Illinois, U.S.A.
Natchez Plantation House
735 North Atlantic Boulevard, Fort Lauderdale, Florida, U.S.A.

© *1966, by* CHARLES C THOMAS • PUBLISHER
Library of Congress Catalog Card Number: 65-27585

*With THOMAS BOOKS careful attention is given to all details of
manufacturing and design. It is the Publisher's desire to present books
that are satisfactory as to their physical qualities and artistic possibilities
and appropriate for their particular use. THOMAS BOOKS will be true
to those laws of quality that assure a good name and good will.*

*Printed in the United States of America*
W-2

To My Parents

# PREFACE

THIS BRIEF TEXT is the result of teaching mental health to university students who seek to understand some of the unpleasant emotional experiences associated with higher education. From the students' classroom queries and their presentation of problems in a university mental health clinic, it has become apparent that something can be done to make known to these students some of the typical emotional difficulties which seem to be spawned in and characteristic of the environment both of a small college and of a large university. Between the well-adjusted students and those torn by conflicts and emotional upheaval, there are a sufficient number who have doubts about themselves, who are confused in their attitudes and their values, but who fail to admit these problems to anyone or to seek professional help and support. Hence, a source of information that sheds light upon these areas of emotional uncertainties should be beneficial.

Although it is recognized that the didactic method in mental health education is not fully effective, nevertheless, to give the student some facts about the concept of normal behavior and to inform him of what he can expect from certain behavior problems that arise in a university setting constitute an effective means for enabling the student to cope with his difficulties in college. There is also the possibility that he can be prepared for professional assistance should the need arise.

The objective of this book, therefore, is to clarify mental health problems for the student and to explain to him the various reasons that keep students from performing adequately. In addition, many misconceptions and erroneous expectations with regard to university mental health teams are eradicated. Much time and effort for both the student and the counselor can be

saved when certain methods of prevention of emotional disturbance are introduced to 'the student and when some preparation
is made regarding the type of difficulty that he may expect to
meet during his college enrollment.

It would be practical if a guide book were available to give
the student some idea about mental symptoms and to offer him
information on how much of the behavior which he considers
peculiar can generally be accepted as normal. Often he may not
know where to go for professional help or what to expect from it.
Although mental health personnel in institutions of higher learning deal with a population different from that of other institutions
and consequently are familiar with the problems characteristic
of this group, so far they have not provided an adequate source
for conveying such information to the student. The availability
of this type of knowledge is highly desirable.

It is the purpose of this book to speak directly to the student
in a language that he understands. Texts on abnormal psychology
or philosophy are often too remote from the student's campus
experiences to give him significant help. Furthermore, most
student emotional difficulties are not grave enough to be classified
as mental illnesses in the strict sense of the word. Of course,
serious mental illnesses are found among students just as among
the general population. Educators and workers in the mental
health services on campus are already familiar with diagnoses,
dispositions, and therapy procedures. As they engage in preventive work through education, they may use this text as an aid
in their work.

Of the great variety of behavior problems typical of the
adolescent and young adult, some seem to be more prevalent
or appear in a more exaggerated form in the college student than
among others of his age. We must bear in mind that a sufficient
number of these difficulties are simply exaggerations of what is
usually understood as normal in the still developing youth. It
is the quality of the additional stress in college that exacerbates
the student's personal difficulties, whether these stem from lack
of talent and interest in academic pursuits or from predisposing
emotional factors. The fact remains that the student needs
assistance, and he can be helped at some time during the span
of his college attendance. It often happens that he learns by

sharing in the experiences of others, or he may eventually solve his problems by trial and error. However, such methods do not always work in his favor.

The scope of this book is to interpret to the student, in a simple and objective way, the problems that are normally found as he is expected to make his new adjustments to the university campus. In many academic failures, an emotional, situational, or a family problem inevitably comes into focus. Since entrance requirements automatically exclude most of the intellectually inferior students, the majority of the student's problems, as seen from the point of view of a typical mental health clinic in a university, are of an emotional or social nature.

The material in this book is not original and it is expressed without the use of technical language, as far as possible. Its contents merely constitute a translation into simple phraseology many of the basic principles of human adjustment which are espoused by the majority of clinicians who work with college students. Most of the material presented in this book is already known to most clinicians. The aim of the present endeavor is to present this information to the college student, so that his own experiences can be related to fundamental concepts which may eventually dispel some of his confusion, and provide answers to any current difficulties that he may experience. Even if the information does not entirely clear up, in his own mind, the nature of his difficulties—for a book cannot substitute for real treatment—at least, he may understand the magnitude of the problem and what it means to him. Finally, he can be in a better position to know what to do about it.

The cases cited in this book have been properly disguised and altered, when necessary, in order to protect the student's confidentiality. Only the significant and pertinent material in these cases was used, material that would be most beneficial to the student. To present, in a brief text such as this, examples of all the possible difficulties that the student may encounter in his college career would obviously be impossible, for many of them are of a vocational nature and are excluded from the domain of mental health. Those which cannot be entirely divorced from a fundamental emotional maladaptation, however, are the problems with which this text proposes to deal.

# ACKNOWLEDGMENTS

THE AUTHOR IS indebted to Dr. T. A. Kiersch, psychiatrist, and Chairman of the Mental Health Division of the University of Illinois Health Center, for improving, revising, and evaluating the manuscript, after critically reading the earlier drafts, and for his continued interest, cooperation, and unlimited encouragement. Acknowledgment is, likewise, expressed to Dr. Orville S. Walters, Director of the University of Illinois Health Center, for his careful and critical reading of Chapter II. The author is also grateful to Dr. Harry Little and Dr. Charles Young, staff psychiatrists in the Mental Health Division who reviewed sections of the draft and offered advice and invaluable comments. For all errors or demerits the author alone is responsible.

Gratitude is here expressed, also, to Mr. Ronald Conant Johnson, of the English Department, for editing the entire manuscript, and for enhancing its continuity and general presentation. Appreciation is also expressed to Mrs. Anne H. Young, secretary of the Mental Health Division, for her splendid patience and efficiency in the typing of the entire manuscript. Finally, with enormous gratitude, the author is indebted to the influence of the many students in the classrooms of mental health lectures for their inspiring and stimulating suggestions, and for contributing many of their ideas and experiences which appear in this book.

A. N.

# CONTENTS

# MENTAL HEALTH
# FOR STUDENTS

# 1

## GENERAL PERSPECTIVES OF MENTAL HEALTH

THE INCREASING CONCERN for the treatment and prevention of emotional illnesses indicates that adjustment to the problems of everyday living by most normal people has been more difficult in the twentieth century than at any previous time. The individual's well-being and happiness, and his personal and social adjustment to his environment are being emphasized more now than ever before. Nearly everyone is aware of the growing problem of mental and emotional maladjustment, and of the role of "bad nerves" and "tensions." Increasingly, large educational, business and governmental institutions in the United States, and in many other parts of the world, are offering advisory and professional services which aim at the prevention of incapacitating emotional conflicts and stress improvement of one's personality for more satisfactory adjustment and effectiveness in solving the problems of life.

The objectives of the following sections of this chapter will be to define and clarify to the student the fundamental characteristics of mental health and to convey a general idea about emotional disturbances found in college students. A general discussion of the nature of personality will also be presented, along with an explanation of the social forces and academic pressures in college responsible for the shaping of the student's personality and for the emotional and intellectual difficulties that he may encounter during his college sojourn.

### Introduction

Colleges and universities have felt the impact of a variety

of problems affecting their students. Many of these institutions are now offering special facilities to help prevent crippling mental symptoms and to assist the student in becoming equipped emotionally and intellectually to face and control the undesirable aspects of adjustment that normally occur when one moves into a new social environment. There is growing recognition of the fact that despite his above-average ability, the student may be faced with academic failure and with difficulty in intellectual functioning when an emotional problem appears. Although there are many textbook sources on general mental health concepts, there is little mental health information, compiled on experiences in college, for the enlightenment of the student.

Many efforts are being made to educate the public and to promote and maintain mental well-being; similar efforts towards these goals are now being introduced to the college student. It would be a mistake to assume that the primary aim of education is the accumulation of facts and knowledge by the student. Making decisions for oneself, meeting the demands and stress of living, establishing goals for the future, and participating in all life's activities, in a world of competiton and conflict, are aspects of behavior which are equally as important to the student as is academic success.

Although the aim of the college environment is to stimulate emotional and intellectual growth, the result is not always in this direction. The student must have a healthy image of himself and must feel confident that he *can* become what he wants to be. If this point has not been clarified after a sufficient time in college, his mental and emotional energy is spent trying to cope with his personal problem, and he will not be able to justify the need for a college education. Another basic problem is the student who is in conflict with instructors and peers, as a result of transferring difficulties with his own parents and siblings to them. If the student matures during college, both such problems will be outgrown; he will become encouraged as his social skills improve, and he will develop new and more satisfying inter-personal relationships.

The emotional problems of students, their symptoms, and treatment procedures employed are essentially the same as those found in the general population. What should be borne in mind, however, is that the predisposing situational conditions in college are not necessarily the same as those found in the general population. Some students have conflicts of long standing that originate in childhood and seem to lie dormant until college, at which time they become overt. Others develop conflicts because of stress in the academic setting which sensitizes some already existing personal inadequacy. This does not mean that the university is the primary cause of conflicts or maladjustments. Nor can we say that just because a student exhibits a physical or intellectual weakness he will necessarily experience failure or some kind of emotional conflict. Usually a combination of several factors, social and personal, is responsible for the student's emotional difficulty.

College life involves more than walking to classes, taking notes, and studying and passing exams. The student is also affected by the social and academic atmosphere, which is not the same in all colleges and universities. It can range from being extremely liberal to extremely conservative. The student should take these factors into account, prior to enrollment, and decide for himself, rather than choose an institution with an ideology opposite to his own. The dissatisfaction that follows a wrong choice often causes the student to complain and to launch verbal criticisms against the system of education, or to remain silent, pretending that all is normal although he feels tense inside. Both conditions can affect him adversely, if he has not been able to compromise with himself after being in college for a reasonable amount of time.

Man has always had to adjust to new situations, such as the student's first experience with college, and has had to learn to solve the problems of living, in order to survive and maintain his personal adjustment and his group's welfare. The human race has struggled constantly against physical and social forces. Emotional maladjustment is often the result of a failure to adjust to these forces. At times, it is manifested as a disease, like a physical illness that requires medical attention; but in most cases, it represents a failure to solve the emotional, psychological, social, ethical, religious, and moral problems affecting the individual.

Most major personal and social problems are, to a large extent, problems related to emotional maladjustment.

Nearly everyone, at one time or another, experiences difficulties brought about by his inability to cope with pressing social situations and with the demands of his everyday life. In most instances, these difficulties are considered to be normal problems of normal people. It is when personal and social conflicts become persistent and exaggerated and interfere with one's activities and effectiveness in life that he is emotionally disturbed. Maladjustment, then, depends more upon the *degree* of psychological handicap in the attainment of one's goals in life than upon the nature of the adjustment problem. Mental health involves the application of psychological principles and experimental findings which will enable maladjusted individuals to lead useful and effective lives and which will prevent mentally healthy persons from becoming maladjusted.

A way to understand emotional disturbances is to consider the extent to which a person or society suffers from a particular type of behavior disorder. Feelings, thoughts and conflicts which may seem inappropriate and unwanted by the student can be looked upon as characteristics of all normal human beings as long as the distress is easily tolerable. Hence, it can be said that individuals with emotional problems are not always abnormal. It is often observed that the individual's *attitude* towards such personality characteristics is unhealthy, rather than the characteristics themselves. If these features are a source of disability and constant unhappiness for the student, to the point where he cannot act to fulfill his mental and emotional capacities, his behavior becomes less normal. The types of disturbances which may arise from stress in college are presented in Chapter 5.

One difficulty in the handling of the student's psychological problem is that there seldom are standard answers and explanations for every symptom of maladjustment. Furthermore, if the same problem is identified in two different persons, the treatment method will not always be identical. Because human behavior is very complex and there are many personality factors operating within the individual at a particular moment, exceptional skill and effort are required for a person to decide which one of these factors is chiefly responsible for the student's manifestation of emotional symptoms. Although the symptoms may appear similar in a number of students, the causes are not always the same. The difficulty of dealing with emotional problems is intensified still more by the fact that even if the reasons for an emotional upheaval are identified, they may turn out to be more apparent than real.

A student cannot be expected to solve his problems by the prescription method nor by reading this brief book. To indicate that a particular problem is the one meant and involved and to specify the causes are not easy tasks, and in many cases, the identification of a problem is merely an approximation to the real difficulty. Contrary to general opinion, the reasons for a student's maladaptive behavior in college cannot always be readily identified. Therefore, it would be safe for the student to assume that the recognition of emotional problems involves a wide range of speculation. Furthermore, when a solution has been found, it may not be apparent to the student.

A recurring misconception among students and laymen is the notion that if a person has a "strong" personality, sufficient intelligence, and will power, he can take care of his problems himself. Such an idea is as absurd as it is to say that a person should be able to remove his own appendix. Whenever psychological help is required, it need not be felt as an admission of personal weakness, any more than would be a visit to a physician.

The main theme in mental health today is to prevent emotional problems from becoming intense and crippling to the student, by helping him to recognize and handle them at an early stage. Most students who have tensions and conflicts are able to function well without the need for professional assistance. However, in addition to the academic burdens, there may be unfulfilled military duty, problems in meeting college expenses, concern for parents' welfare, anxiety about employment after leaving college, temporary marital disharmony in the case of married students whose spouses are employed—all fairly realistic problems. These stresses are transitory and can be solved by the students themselves. However, when severe mental and physical symptoms develop which disable the student, professional consultation becomes very helpful.

Hopefully, the student can realize that the thoughts and

feelings which arise from various pressures of higher education are not uniquely his and that his psychological reactions to stress situations are to be accepted. The student does not need to worry about symptoms, if he can see how they happen to be connected to some personal feeling or unpleasant situation. Most complaints presented by college students are based not so much on the real cause, such as a stressful situation, as on the symptoms resulting from the cause. The typical symptoms of the emotionally disturbed student—tension, depression, and physical complaints—are discussed in Chapter 5.

## The Meaning of Personality

Professional workers in the field of mental health are constantly dealing with the development, the measurement, and the understanding of personality, and are trying to utilize the most effective ways of changing it in the direction of the student's optimum adjustment. Psychology is still unable to formulate an accurate definition of personality; however, it can be said in simple terms that those factors which make one person behave *differently* from another tell us the kind of personality he has. Different people adjust to their environments in different ways. There is no single trait, habit, or temperament that accounts for a student's adjustment; on the contrary, there are a large number of learned and innate personal factors and a large variety of social environments which explain why a person behaves the way he does at a particular moment. The student's early life experiences, his relationship with his parents, the number of siblings in his family, the type of neighborhood in which he has resided, the social status and education of his parents, and a host of other factors all contribute to the formation of his personality.

One important psychological principle of human behavior stresses the uniqueness of the individual personality: no two people can be exactly alike. Many people may have similar traits of personality or some kind of special aptitude; yet, the quality of these elements and the way in which they are interwoven with the rest of the personality account largely for personality differences. We can find an analogy in fingerprints; although tens of thousands appear similar, no two fingerprints are ever exactly alike.

Personality differences result from inherited factors and from learned or acquired characteristics. A person's physique, intelligence, academic training, social environment, habits, skills, emotions, motives, interests—all contribute to the shaping of his personality. Since these factors are not the same with all people, it follows that the shaping of personalities will vary. Whether a person's behavior is basically inherited or acquired later in life through learning is still a controversial question; however, most psychologists agree that both factors play a significant role. For example, an intellectually bright boy without exposure to educational advantages may appear "average"; whereas a person with only an average endowment may do very well academically, when placed in an intellectually stimulating environment.

A student may come closer to an understanding of his behavior in college if he has some knowledge of the functions of the human mind. The mind or psyche is divided, generally, into the *conscious* and *unconscious* segments, and each of these is again divided into many minor parts. The conscious mind functions consciously, i.e., the student is aware of what he is doing, and he has knowledge of his everyday life. The unconscious mind contains those aspects of the student's personality of which he is unaware: drives, needs, wishes, and conflicts which have existed since infancy but whose presence is no longer known by the student. The unconscious also includes those experiences which happened during the span of his life but have been forgotten. The division of the mind is more artificial than real. The conscious and unconscious portions are actually different states or degrees of the same activity. The influence of the unconscious portion of the mind cannot be ascertained except by analysis of the student's behavior. For example, the student who claims that he loves his girlfriend and goes out of his way to say kind things and to verbalize his love in strong terms may simultaneously be acting in a way that annoys and alienates her from him. From this, it can be speculated that he resents her, and the motives for his behavior can be examined.

From the foregoing, it becomes evident that a large portion of the student's behavior is influenced by unconscious factors in that his behavior cannot be entirely understood by taking into account the known facts. For example, the real reasons for a student's wanting to study medicine rather than philosophy—besides his stated interest—may be unconscious. Of course, there is no need for him to know why he made this choice, as long as he is satisfied with it. The student should be cautioned not to engage in extensive self-examination with the purpose of finding out why he acts as he does, if his behavior is not entirely satisfying to him. Too much introspection may be harmful, and the student may become more confused. The best he can do, should there be a need for greater self-understanding, is to consult an expert; in many cases what he thinks to be "wrong" about himself is harmless and of minor consequence. Experience attests to the fact that a detached and skilled "outsider" can be of great assistance. Even the most skillful practitioners hesitate to treat their own ailments; for instance, a physician with a heart ailment consults a heart specialist, despite what he may already know about his own heart.

Although unconscious factors may be causing problems which cannot be explained on the basis of the given facts about the student's past and present life experiences, it is not always correct to attribute to unconscious reasons all the student's behavior problems and thus absolve him from responsibility. Of course, a great variety of students' problems, such as inability to study, hostility towards others, and sensitivity to rejection by the opposite sex, may be symptomatic of a serious underlying difficulty of which the student is unaware. After a therapist has identified the problems and made them explicit in the student's mind, they can often be worked out by stressing to the student his own responsibility for his actions. The role of therapists in mental hygiene is explained in Chapter 7.

## The Results of Social Change

The world in which we live does not remain constant. In all aspects of life there is continuous change, which requires certain accommodations and flexibility when adaptation is desired. Those students who have rigid personalities will have difficulty making adjustments, such as changing to a different environment. If the student's personality is geared to harmonize with the new changes, he is less likely to feel stress. The student should be expected to forfeit a few of the values and attitudes he learned during the earlier phases of his life, in order to acquire new ones that will be more beneficial and will bring him to terms with the demands of college life. Besides the change occasioned by the transition from high school to college, society itself, as we shall see, has undergone a fundamental change, which has affected the mode of education and the character of social relationships in college.

Since the turn of the century, North America has undergone important sociological changes that have affected the individual's adjustment to the newly emerging problems of living. The most significant social change is the transition from an *autocratic* to a *democratic* concept of life. The former is characteristic of authoritarian attitudes in society and family. In such a society, the majority was obligated to follow the rules set by a few. Social classes were stagnant and structured to the extent that very few members were able to move into another class. Choices of work, education and marriage were limited. Each person knew his role and social position. Consequently, conflicts were relatively few in this autocratic environment.

When society began to put in effect the democratic principles of equal opportunity and equal privileges for all, changes came at such a rapid pace that many people were unable to cope with them. In a business-democracy, everyone can strive to "prove" himself or to obtain a higher position in society. Democratic philosophy stresses competition; this, in turn, produces failures, which are frequently associated with anxiety, feelings of worthlessness, and a sense of personal inadequacy.

Democracy implies that everyone has the same rights and equal chances; the by-products of this way of life are competition, aggression, and a need to excel. Every student is certainly aware of these factors. Many students have to act defensively in their interpersonal relationships, in order to pursue their own goals. Such behavior creates additional problems in the students, such as depression and anxiety, which cripple his adjustment and functioning in college. By understanding these social relationships, one can see why campus living can be a significant source of stress for the student who has not been prepared for it.

There are other apparent academic and social characteristics of college which are relatively different from those typical in high school. In the former, for instance, the student is given greater personal responsibility, and he is expected to reach his own decisions; but in high school, parents and teachers assume many responsibilities and supervise student decisions. Furthermore, the student on the American campus today is living through an era and is confronted with experiences startlingly different from those of a half century ago. The mode of campus living has changed, the style of instruction has been modified, specialization has altered the aims of education, social standards have evolved, and the attitude toward higher education is not the same as it was a few decades ago.

Not only must he change outwardly to meet the new college environment, but the student must allow a certain amount of change to come from *within*. When he enters college, he soon realizes that he must give up some of his immature behavior and "grow up." This process requires change which is often accompanied by discontent, self-criticism, self-doubt, and anxiety. The student should realize that these feelings are characteristic of any person who undergoes a change, and are not considered as being entirely his own "fault." Somehow, college reminds the student that his boyhood, carefree days are gone, and that from now on he has to "buckle down." Because of these feelings, some students become timid, while others become hostile and aggressive; still others harbor mixed feelings toward the whole idea of obtaining a college education.

For most students, these adverse consequences are very mild, and they become extinct as the student becomes proficient in social and academic skills; he forms acquaintances with similar interests, and he embarks on a routine study pace. As the initial impact fades away, he no longer feels injured in his self-esteem nor unwanted. As new demands appear, he is ready to make the proper adjustments to meet them. Likewise, once he forms a major goal he automatically develops new skills to implement his goal. He realizes that he is not going to be a student all of his life, and that his few years in college are merely a "stepping stone" towards more remote objectives.

There are many kinds of emotional stress traceable to changes that have occurred on college campuses in the past few decades. An increasing number of students commute to college or live together in limited space. These students who must function on a regulated schedule and with a more or less new type of conformity are likely to feel restrictions in conjunction with the pressure of college work. Large enrollments may necessitate regimentation for better control. Under these conditions, the student has to organize himself in order to cope with deadlines, to endure social restraints, and to meet with new obligations. As a result of his inability to adapt to these new changes, after having left the comfort of the home environment, he may react with a variety of symptoms. For example, he may blame the college for his feeling of being a mere "number" and relatively unknown to the campus community. Such elements can certainly make the student resentful, angry, or withdrawing, and as he becomes emotionally uncomfortable, his academic performance can deteriorate.

The consequence of these conditions is the development of strong feelings of inferiority and inadequacy. Social competition becomes just as important as the desire for good grades. Some students develop a pattern of aggresive behavior in order to cover up their basic inferiority, while others give up the struggle, waiting to be helped, or collect injustices to rationalize their failure.

Many students perform well in nearly all phases of academic work but simultaneously feel unsure of themselves and are not nearly so convinced of their success as others assume them to be. These students suffer from feelings of inferiority which they have not been able to overcome. When the student is doing well and there is little stress involved, these feelings are pushed into the background. But when his tasks become insurmountable for a while, or even when he finds himself with nothing to do, feelings and thoughts of uncertainty and pessimism, and the questioning of his real motives and ability for college work come into the foreground.

The college student, being in his late adolescence and early adult years, is treated as a mature adult and is expected to act like one, although in reality he may not be fully matured emotionally and intellectually. His college years provide an opportunity for him to make many advancements toward maturity. Throughout the course of his schooling, he begins to substitute for his fantasies actual participation in the social and academic areas of college life. He becomes less emotionally inhibited, and he learns to express his feelings with regulation. Finally, he becomes less sensitive to his felt intellectual and physical shortcomings, and he subordinates his own welfare to the welfare of society. Thus, he progresses toward maturity as the result of his college experience.

One expects a student to have occasional doubts regarding his ability to achieve his objectives in college. Life would be uninteresting, if all the problems of living were suddenly solved. These uncertainties can serve as a challenge for self-understanding, provided that the student avoids excessive introspection. If the student's doubts become strongly personal and subjective, and if they emanate from a deeper problem, he is likely to feel more handicapped than the one whose doubts are objective and realistic. For example, there is a difference between the student who has doubts concerning failure, despite his close-to-an-A average, and the one who has doubts about obtaining a scholarship because of the large number of applicants in proportion to the limited number of available scholarships. The increase of maturity and knowledge helps the student overcome the doubts created by the transition to college. As the "shock" eventually diminishes, he gains more confidence and learns to cope with competitiveness in college through *cooperation* toward goals favorable both to himself and to society.

The beginning college student may soon find that some activities and courses he liked in high school will no longer hold his interest in college. Moreover, because it may be the first time that he has lived with people other than members of his immediate family, he often finds the social conduct, thinking, and interests of many students quite different from his own, because of various social and geographical factors. This is especially true in a large university. Large enrollments involve a great variety of students and create conditions which make the individual student increasingly aware of his own behavior, as he notices how his fellow students react toward him. These experiences can be managed relatively easily, if the student takes a constructive attitude and if he has learned to accept the idea that other students are not always going to make allowances for him. These diverse characteristics may not be found in students attending small sectarian colleges, since their social background, their personal aspirations, and, in some cases, their religion would tend to be similar.

The student just out of high school is prone to envision college as a continuous series of successes devoid of impediments and frustrations. He becomes easily attached to the belief that he will pass his exams with flying colors, have many interesting dates, be admired by peers, attain excellence in athletics, and so on, only to become disillusioned when he arrives on the college scene. If these attitudes are strong and not amenable to change, the student will have considerable difficulty making an initial adjustment to college. The challenge for the college student is not so much how well he will succeed but whether he is capable of yielding to new influences and of being responsive to changing conditions.

## What Is Mental Health?

The transition to college can make the student feel so uncomfortable that he may even begin to look for "symptoms" and "complexes" and often convince himself that he has actually found them. But even if they do exist, they do not always mean maladjustment. Mental health does not imply the absence of conflicts and emotional problems; nor is it simply a general state of personal contentment, satisfaction, and peace of mind. Ability to relate well with other people, to take things calmly, and to avoid worry are certainly desirable characteristics of mental health, but they are concepts too simple, superficial, and unsophisticated for the college student.

The concept of mental health encompasses many other meanings which are more important than those mentioned above.

The mentally healthy student accepts himself with his strong points *and* his shortcomings; he makes the best use of what he has, and he does not allow his personal weaknesses to interfere with his daily activities and his pursuit of long-range goals. If the positive factors in his personality are accentuated, the weaknesses, in most cases, will retreat from the foreground. The emotionally healthy student reaches a balance between his instincts and his conscience, coupled with the demands of his environment. He experiences little conflict between these feelings, and he can tolerate a moderate amount of inconvenience resulting from conflicts among drives, values, and the experiences of reality in the academic environment.

Selfishness; a strong need for affection, without the ability to reciprocate; the aiming for immediate gratification of personal needs; lack of self-control; and responding with anger or depression when emotional supplies are not provided—all these suggest poor emotional health. The student may not even be aware of these inappropriate emotional responses until he meets with a major failure and begins to realize that his adjustment has been faulty. Students who are characterized by these qualities are unable to manipulate the obstacles that come in their way and cannot make effective use of their abilities. The process of overcoming obstacles by manipulating the environment should always involve consideration of the welfare of others.

On the other hand, the showing of deep emotions without becoming overwhelmed by them, the finding of satisfaction in a variety of interests, and the giving of meaning to one's activities indicate a high degree of emotional health. Students possessing such qualities are likely to integrate new experiences, are able to solve most problems as they come, and, at the same time, are able to develop their potentials and talents. They can laugh at their mistakes and appraise their abilities fairly well, and they have a feeling of responsibility for and interest in other students.

The emotional well-being of the student in higher education is becoming a matter of concern to many educators. The still unsettled process of physical maturation, the question of a vocational choice the independence from parents, the seeking of values and goals in life, and the conciliation between social pressure and personal needs are conscious problems of the student. Since these patterns are very typical of late adolescence and young adulthood, workers in the field of mental health are interested in making the student understand them by applying the knowledge that is already available on these problems. The prevention of emotional maladjustments through education can be an easier task in the university or college than in nonacademic institutions, because students are more prone to accept new and challenging ideas. Students should understand that many emotional problems are not really "mental illnesses," in the ordinary sense of the word, but are conditions aggravated by stresses arising from being in the college situation and from the process of maturing.

Most students are able to make the transition from high school to college and to overcome the strain involved in meeting the new environment without great difficulty. There are some, however, who experience this change with a profound emotional shock, especially if their values from home do not coincide with those of the academic milieu. The word value in the present context, implies the student's attitude towards things, activities, or ideas which he appreciates, esteems highly, and considers worthy of pursuit. The best solution, in the case of conflicting values, is for the student to attempt a fusion between the two extremes, rather than to give up totally one system of values in favor of the other. Yet, even this simple approach may be difficult for some students. Both the home environment and the academic institutions have significant values to offer, values which are often essentially quite similar, and the wise student can make the best use of them.

Mild peculiarities in the student's behavior, as long as they do not prevent him from functioning adequately, enhance the uniqueness of his personality and make him appear more interesting to others. The student is not expected to adjust to all the unpleasant conditions in college; in fact, the difficulties he encounters should serve as stimuli for the creation of greater motivation towards self-advancement. No one can possibly be constantly happy; also, occasional and moderate fluctuations in mood are very natural feelings, which should be accepted by every student. These factors are mentioned here because many students, at some time during the span of their college attendance, complain about them. These feelings and thoughts should be tolerated as long as they do not become continuous and bothersome. When they do, psychological help is beneficial and justified.

When the student examines his past behavior, he is likely to find himself unable to explain some of his actions and reactions to different situations. He may think that he acted unwisely, and that if he were to go through the same situation again, he would now act differently. This experience is very common, and it is a basic attitude of the normal personality. It also indicates that under normal conditions, one is not expected to know all his motives and reasons for behaving as he does. Furthermore, to be able to recognize later some of the things he did in the past and to laugh at his awkwardness and mistakes constitute sound mental health. It is only when the student dwells on one unfortunate event that he is apt to be considered ill-adjusted. The student should feel fortunate if he can recall some of the childish things he did in the past and say to himself with amusement, "How could I possibly have done a silly thing like that?"

Refraining from behavior that society does not tolerate, displaying a reasonable amount of conformity without sacrificing one's individuality, and feeling respect for logical and realistic authority are characteristic of maturity and of emotional health in the student. A reasonable amount of sensitivity towards social and educational injustices, accompanied by a constructive attitude of criticism, can be a healthy mode of expression. Faultfinding because of resentment over personal injustices rather than for improving others and society is not a very effective technique for bettering one's situation.

University students frequently are troubled with basic philosophical and religious problems of life, feel lonesome and depressed, worry excessively over relatively trivial matters, cannot make decisions, and lack a sense of direction in their education and in their goals in life. Some feel socially unaccepted and lack the friendship that they basically desire. There is no doubt that even those who are considered to be well-adjusted have had such feelings at some time during their life span. Naturally, it is difficult to think that there are persons who have all the characteristics of mental health at all times, just as it is difficult to think of persons who have never had any mild physical disturbance.

Some students make extensive efforts to assure themselves that they are not "unusual," and spend lengthy periods in self-analysis to see if they fit into some ideal pattern of normality. In most cases, these efforts stem from the student's dissatisfaction or failure in some current undertaking. These difficulties are not so much the result of a "neurosis" or "maladjustment" as they are of the student's attitude, learning from past experiences, and inadequate social and academic skills. The majority of such students improve when these aforementioned factors are studied and modified. Occasionally, the student will display childish behavior and appear eccentric. The same can happen to his parents, his teachers, and to any adult; yet, such behavior can be perfectly normal as long as his abilities are not thwarted, and his behavior benefits himself and others.

Feelings of discontent and unhappiness should be considered as typically associated with the conditions of university life. The student should accept a moderate amount of these uneasy feelings as normal reactions to the pressures of college life. It is not uncommon for students to ponder a great deal about what they should do and often complain that things are not sufficiently ideal for anyone who wants to accomplish anything significant. In college, as in any other life situation, students should accept some amount of discomfort as being logically related with any worthwhile goal.

Throughout the history of mankind there have been attempts to reconcile the divergence of the actual world and the ideal one. With reference to the academic setting, this gap can be narrowed if students show a constructive involvement in and a sense of commitment toward their work. It is very common for students to say that they want to "be somebody" and to "do something worthwhile" in life; yet, they may be fulfilling this desire mainly in their daydreams. Since this is a common phenomenon among college students, the following chapters will attempt to clarify and explain to the student some of the more common reasons why he cannot become deeply interested in his work, despite his expressed desire. An institution of higher learning is certainly not always ideal for everyone. The well-motivated student, however, will make use of what he finds available in his academic environment, as long as the future rewards are significant and his goals are meaningful. The significance of goals in the student's life will become clear in Chapter 2.

Human living cannot be conceived of without interpersonal relationships. When people come into contact with one another, there is a mutual influence among them, whether they consciously realize it or not. Consequently, a positive and constructive attitude and an interest in the activities of other students will result in the lessening of tensions and will facilitate the process of adaptation in college. The aim of mental health education is to make the student feel that he is responsible for what he does, and to enable him to make his own decisions for himself. Although he is encouraged to obtain advice and to act on the basis of facts, the final decision should come from himself, and he should be prepared to face the consequences.

There is a growing trend among the members of professional fields dealing with mental health problems to educate and inform the college student by inculcating healthy attitudes toward the mental and emotional maladjustments afflicting him. He must realize that education is not merely the accumulation of data; it involves adjustment to reality by developing sound attitudes that are compatible with factual knowledge about solving problems of human adjustment. By familiarizing himself with general concepts of mental health, he develops a realistic attitude toward the causes and effects of maladjustment. He becomes more sophisticated and less perplexed toward everyday problems, and he can be oriented as to when he should seek help and what to expect from it. As with courses dealing with general notions of hygiene, so with mental health, the student is not expected to treat his ailments but to learn something more about their nature and to take preventive measures. The student can be relieved as he learns that human behavior is not always well understood even by the experts in the field. On the other hand, certain aspects of his behavior which were considered to be complex and incomprehensible to him can be made to be fairly simple and easily understood.

Caution must be taken when the student strongly identifies himself with a problem cited in this text or when he finds a paragraph that describes exactly how he feels and behaves. If such a problem did not bother him to any great extent before he encountered it in his reading, he should not feel now that "something is wrong." The description of these emotional conditions is designed for the student to understand himself— to be assured that a large portion of his behavior is quite normal— and not for him to make a clinical case of himself.

This book is not designed to give advice to students and to offer prescriptions for their troubles. Its primary aim is to give the student an idea about how the human personality works, feels, and acts as he does. In this way, he learns to understand his behavior; but knowledge alone about human behavior will not change the student or cure him of his problems. For any significant change to occur, one needs an *emotional interpersonal experience,* as in a private talk with a psychologist or psychiatrist. Otherwise, people would recover merely by reading books.

Although through reading the student can learn how his mind functions and how his emotions influence his behavior, he will not be transformed into a new person simply by reading about human behavior. He should keep in mind that a book on the adjustive difficulties of students must deal mostly with general tendencies, overlooking the specific situations. However, by gaining a broad knowledge and insight into his behavior, he can form positive attitudes about himself, and can develop more self-esteem. As he becomes more aware of himself, he will be prone to feel more at ease in the college community. By knowing general principles, he can manage with his own specific conditions. Indeed, awareness of one's behavior is the first step toward wisdom.

Finally, consideration must be given to the question of whether the mental health of the individual student is ultimately a personal responsibility or the responsibility of the academic institution which has accepted him as a student. Undoubtedly, views on this issue will differ. However, if education aims at the student's mental and emotional development and the growth of personal responsibility, then both the academic institution and the student should be concerned. If treatment facilities are available, the student must first assume some responsibility for treatment, before the college is going to assist him with his personal problem. There are exceptions, for example, when the student's behavior is dangerous either to himself or to others. In such a case, there is no choice for the college administration other than to take the necessary protective action, and to solicit health authorities to make the proper medical recommendations.

With proper cooperation between the university or college which provides mental health facilities, and the student who understands how to avail himself of these facilities, much can be achieved in the prevention of emotional turmoil in the college student.

# 2

## THE EMOTIONAL BEHAVIOR OF THE STUDENT

THE STUDENT WILL make an easier adjustment to his new life not only by realizing what he can expect to meet in college, but also by understanding better his own nature as a person and the characteristics of his developing personality. His needs, goals, values, and self-identity have an enormous influence on his social and academic performance in college; and the better he understands them, the easier will be his adaptation. The purpose of the present chapter is to deal specifically with these typical areas of emotional adjustment, in order to make the student aware of them and of their important role in his desire for academic success.

### The Nature of Adolescence

Adolescence, the years between the early teens and early twenties, is a turbulent period for persons in our society. Since a large portion of the college population falls within this age range, it can be helpful for students to recognize and understand some typical characteristics of the adolescent. The following discussion will include those characteristics of behavior in the adolescent which are the outgrowth of his relationship to his parents, for they play an important role in the life of the adolescent attending college. Although most students have been or are currently subjected to these adolescent experiences, normally, very few students actually require intensive or extensive treatment, other than by simply expressing themselves to a responsible adult and feeling accepted and understood.

The student's first encounter with college occurs at a time

in his life before he has developed into complete manhood; yet, neither is he a youngster. He is more or less away from parental control, and he is now, more than ever before, expected to depend upon his own creative resources in adapting to new situations. The closer emotionally he has been toward his parents, the more he is apt to experience uncomfortable feelings associated with his separation from home. The freshman student may feel an urge to quit college for a while in order to "grow up" or he may become "homesick" for a short period during which his grades may suffer. The adjustment that the student tries to make in order to cope with the first impact of college can vary, depending on the type of student and the nature of his problems. Some of the solutions may be self-defeating. The best guarantee for solving the problems is to face the issues involved, rather than avoid them.

Along with his own intellectual endowments, the student brings his feelings, attitudes, and experiences from the past onto the scene of the university, and he is expected to integrate them with those that he will find in the university milieu. It is important that the student be prepared to accept new attitudes and values in college, without violating or discarding his own basic beliefs which were formed through parental influence. The better-adjusted student is the one who can find some sort of continuity in his life between his precollege and college experiences.

Some students continue to display adolescent behavior even though they are chronologically older. Often the student's feeling of inability "to make it through" in college and his anticipation of failure, which is unrealistic if he happens to be a fairly good student, arise merely because he is reacting to adult problems with the attitude of an adolescent. Discouragement from past failures, and the conscious or unconscious desire to remain at an earlier stage of maturity because it makes fewer demands on the student, may cause him to shun the responsibilities that are expected of his age. After a few sessions with a trained counselor, many students respond favorably to encouragement and face their responsibilities with the conviction that they will succeed.

The adolescent has a tendency to reject the values and

attitudes of his parents for a while and to espouse those of his peer group of which he feels to be an accepted member. This period is a very trying one to the parents, especially to those who feel insecure and do not realize that their offspring are learning to become young adults searching for independence. Many parents cannot accept this normal emancipation and often feel guilty about their supposed inability to discipline their children. Instead of accepting the changes in behavior as a normal part of adolescent growth, they frequently attribute this change in the adolescent to their own personality weakness and their inability to exert control over their children.

Part of the adolescent rebellion, which is characteristic of the student's reluctance to go along with his parents' values and admonitions, signifies the student's need to deny his dependency on his parents because that dependency may imply a personality weakness. Hence, he must do the opposite of what his parents expect. For instance, the student whose father is a physician may want to go into some business of his own despite his father's wishes. By realizing that his father once chose his career, the son feels he is losing his right as a person to choose his own profession.

During the period of adolescence, there is a tendency for the girl to be responsive to her father's warmth, and she looks for his acceptance. The girl who feels appreciated by her father and develops a sense of personal worth finds it easier to make successful heterosexual social relationships outside of the home. The mother may often feel threatened and resentful of her daughter's attraction to the father, but it is finally the mother who gives the daughter the image of feminine adulthood. A somewhat similar relationship develops with the adolescent boy. He has a tendency to become antagonistic toward the father and closer to the mother. As he becomes more mature, he seeks independence from her and finds more satisfying social relationships with females outside his home environment.

At this age the sexual drives reach their peak, but intellectual maturity is still developing. Under these conditions, the adolescent has more difficulty resisting his own passions and channeling his impulses into activity that is useful and socially acceptable.

Everyone has impulses, but the reason some persons express them is because of inability to control them. Those who do not ordinarily manifest impulses are not necessarily devoid of them; they simply restrain and regulate them within certain normal limits. The student should not be alarmed about harboring phantasies in which he acts out his impulses, as long as he does not express them in real life. If everyone enacted what he really thought, the university population would be a very unmanageable lot. Dreams and daydreaming are frequent outlets for these impulses which society does not condone.

Learning new, acceptable, sexual roles and attaining hetero-sexual adjustment is also characteristic of adolescence. Some males remain dependent on their mothers and cannot properly relate themselves to the opposite sex. If one does find a dating partner, she is certain to be identified with his mother. She would be the one most likely to direct the conversation and make decisions on the date. A female student often prefers a date several years her senior, so that she can remain the baby and relate to him as she did to her own father. Many students, however, outgrow these tendencies in adulthood. Normally, every adult has a few minor adolescent features in his behavior which are barely noticeable. On the other hand, some students may already be in their adult years and still be struggling with adolescent problems. It is with these latter cases that psy-chological help is most beneficial.

New interests begin to develop in this period, but many of them are discarded as soon as the novelty has worn off. Interest in physical skills is more pronounced, as is sensitivity about the physique and the body's general appearance. There is a greater interest in the opposite sex, and a tendency to be guided and impressed by external appearance. There is also considerable fluctuation in mood, temper, aspirations, and in many attitudes toward life in general. Adolescence is a period of instability and of many inconsistencies in goals and decisions. Finally, there is the choice of a role. Usually, the adolescent tries out many roles which are often incompatible with his real self and as he reaches maturity he adapts to and integrates the new adult role.

Compared to the younger years, minor emotional disturbances are more apt to be felt at the onset of the adolescent years. The adolescent meets with unprecedented difficulties, because of his greater freedom of choice and action which he discovers once he leaves the home environment. Despite the psychological pressure from college, the overall effect of attending an educational institution is to solidify and integrate the student. His life is "put together," so to speak, and his abilities are organized to help him accomplish something meaningful for his future.

## Psychological Needs of the Student

Fulfillment of one's emotional needs in socially acceptable ways is the fundamental principle of mental health. These needs are usually developed by the standards of values of our society, and their aim is to help the student survive in and adjust to his college environment. Different people have different needs, which, as a rule, originate in early childhood. It is the manner in which the student attempts to satisfy them that classifies his behavior as more or less normal. Conflict of psychological needs often results in frustration, guilt, depression or anxiety, and in many such cases, some kind of outside professional consultation is quite helpful. In spite of the diversity of emotional needs, there are certain psychological elements present in nearly all persons, in some form or another. The following discussion will present a few of the most significant psychological needs of the student.

Just as the body has physical needs which require fulfillment so that the human organism can survive and function, so there are psychological needs which also must be satisfied. Every person desires to be accepted for himself by those with whom he associates and identifies. He wants to feel useful and needed by his associates and to know that he is as good as they are. When he feels disapproved of, he wants to know that it is due to the things he does and not to the way he is. Many educators and mental health authorities emphasize love as the basic human need that should be given primary consideration above all other psychological needs.

It is generally agreed that the need for *affection* is the

strongest. Children grow faster emotionally when affection is present during the period of their emotional development. If the child has been deprived of affection, his intellectual functioning may also be affected; that is, his strong emotional needs become of such concern to him that they divert his energy and attention from his intellectual capabilities. Those who were not accorded love during their childhood may have some difficulty reciprocating affection in their adulthood and may feel unworthy of love, or they may become emotionally distant and aloof. They may also degrade those who happen to be fairly spontaneous with their emotions, and may even be suspicious and envious of them. Since the ability to love is learned, the learning process can still take place belatedly in adulthood.

The university atmosphere provides a great deal of intellectual stimulation, which often results in neglecting the student's emotional needs. But nature has created man to desire closeness. Although most students are able to satisfy these needs to a reasonable degree, there are always a few who become confused and anxious when faced with emotionally provoking situations. For example, when someone expresses affection for them, they become anxious and cannot respond with the same feelings. There are several reasons for this kind of behavior, the most important ones being his fear that he may become too dependent on someone else, his apprehension over the possibility that if he does express himself he may go too far, and his belief that emotionality is usually associated with a weak character, i.e., that only inferior persons manifest emotions. Still others look upon themselves as being so inferior that they do not deserve any affection. It is not uncommon for this type of student to become frightened when someone shows him affection even merely with endearing words.

Every person, whether he realizes it or not, is constantly striving to maintain himself in a state of harmony with his environment which provides favorable conditions for his emotional growth. This implies the notion of *security*. In all aspects of life, whether political, social, or economic, security is a psychological need that contributes to one's welfare and sense of well-being. Everyone wants to feel sure he is living in a safe place, and that there will be resources available to render help should he come upon a crisis. Security also means protection and removal from strange, frightening or unknown situations.

The role of individual rights is an important aspect of our culture. Normal people want to be *recognized* as persons in their own right and to have a feeling of personal worth and identity. Recognition, in our culture, is associated with success and a sense of belonging, and enhances one's notion about his abilities and personal esteem. In order for one to attain these attitudes and feel *significant,* he must act in a way that is favorable and beneficial to others. A person's concept of himself depends upon what he *means* to others. There is an implication here that one cannot satisfy these needs without coming into close contact and relating to others.

Another important psychological need is the student's feeling of *self-confidence,* of being able to rely on his own resources for making responsible decisions which affect his daily life and ultimately his future. This need implies that he must graciously accept his limitations and make the best use of his assets. He must become contented when he performs what he is able to do, for his own sake and for the benefit of mankind. The more the student accepts himself as he really is, the easier it is for him to have self-respect and to accept the limitations he notices in other people. When the student has not come to grips with himself, he is more likely to be dissatisfied and critical of others.

Finally, a need that we cannot escape admitting is the tendency to be interested in *new experiences* in life and to explore the unknown facets of our milieu. Obviously, this need varies greatly from person to person, but we all occasionally want to leave the routine aspects of our daily lives and to seek unique experiences that give us a sense of pleasure. From this brief survey of psychological needs, the reader can begin to understand why they are so important for the development of sound mental health.

Those who have not learned to become emotionally warm and close to others are basically unhappy persons. The student has needs, not only intellectual but also emotional. Development and specialization in a specific academic area is only a one-sided approach to the student's needs. Self-understanding and knowing how to get along with other people are aspects of the student's behavior which he has not been taught systematically. The result is that the student may satisfy his intellectual and vocational needs yet remain underdeveloped in the emotional area. The outcome is that the student searches for outlets to express some of his emotional needs, and he has a desire to confide in someone. It remains up to the student himself to find ways to replenish his psychological needs through social responsiveness.

At times, we all feel like talking and sharing our experiences with someone we trust, without fear of being ridiculed or rejected. This need to *confide* and *communicate* with someone and feel happy in his presence is usually gratified with the marriage bond.

What has just been said is common to the majority of college students. Some manage successfully to make emotional ties with other people, but others try to "forget" these needs and pretend that they do not exist in them. Such students may eventually make attempts to cope with these problems by discussing them either with a faculty member or a counselor. Some students would prefer to discuss first a more immediate problem, frequently of an academic nature, as an attempt to avoid the embarrassment of stating the real emotional problem. Fortunately, most college students do have the capacity to relate to someone, when a permissive, encouraging, and nonthreatening opportunity is offered to them, although some may require more time than others. The student must first understand what he is expected to gain by confiding to someone, and why this process in itself is, in most instances, emotionally beneficial to him.

### Feelings of Inferiority

From their experience in clinical practice, many professional workers in mental hygiene believe that the basic element of man's personality is a deep feeling of personal *inferiority*. It is manifested in his struggle to control the forces of nature and to master himself as well as the destiny of his fellow man. Inferiority stems mainly from man's inability to maintain adequate control over the natural forces outside of himself and, according to theologians, from his inferior position to his Creator. As a child, he sees himself small and fragile in relation to his parents and adults, and if this feeling persists, he frequently feels inferior as an adult.

What has just been said applies directly to the college student, whether he lives on campus or not. The university fosters a spirit of rivalry, which implies that the student must strive to excel if he wants to survive in the academic setting. This struggle seems to describe best the conditions and the framework in which the student's psychological symptoms are formed. When many persons compete to attain the same goals, there is bound to be a large number who will feel that they have not gained what they have been striving for. Others will harbor the thought that they will eventually fail despite the fact that they have no current difficulty.

Human nature entails a constant striving for personal growth and for the development of personality according to what society expects and approves. A person feels more inferior to others when he begins to see himself as an unfit member of his social group. Such feelings prompt him either to try harder and appear better in the eyes of others or to give up entirely so that others will do his work for him. If the striving is unacceptable to society and it is against the welfare of others, then we say that his behavior is socially maladjusted. Most people, however, find their place in society, share its values, and feel a part of the world in which they live.

There is no student who does not want to feel accepted, who does not want to be in the right place in college. Those who happen to develop difficulties often compare themselves to other students, with the result that they reach their own conclusions of their worth. These self-estimates are made mostly on a subjective basis and are apt to be misleading. Hence, when the student makes mistakes and encounters failures, he automatically looks upon himself as inferior to those who did not have these experiences, and, consequently, he sees them as superior to himself. The process becomes more exaggerated when the student is already sensitive about his abilities, whether they are social or academic. The student should not underestimate himself simply because he happens to have faults and is occasionally unsuccessful. If he examines himself carefully, he will find that he, too, possesses capabilities. Whether or not he feels inferior depends upon his attitude toward himself, rather than upon the actual unfortunate events that he remembers most vividly.

The high academic standards and social expectations that confront the student make his social and academic survival a more difficult problem to surmount. They create an undertone of rivalry and an effort on the part of the student to equal and excel. Under these conditions, the student becomes success-conscious and failure-conscious. When he begins to feel the pressure in college, he develops feelings of inadequacy and defeat. In order to overcome these feelings, he can do a number of things: criticize the school and instructors, play the role of the sufferer, set up very high standards for himself so that he can force others to feel inadequate, or retreat from involvement to avoid failure. A typical example of the latter reaction is the student who prefers not to study and thus receive a failing grade, because if he should study and still fail, it would mean that he is inadequate. The ideal situation, of course, is that in which feelings of inferiority motivate the student as a form of challenge toward success. He is at liberty to make up for his feelings of inferiority. Chapter 4 will be devoted to the typical psychological devices which protect the student's personality from anxiety and feelings of inferiority.

The student should accept the idea that feelings of inferiority are experienced in every normal person. On account of his age and relatively limited experience, the college student is not yet expected to feel a full sense of accomplishment and belonging-ness to the adult world. However, when feelings of inferiority become strong, the individual's personality automatically uses devices which lessen them, in the same manner that antibodies are produced in order to combat the germs which enter the human body. When the personality, for various reasons, has not been able to create devices to protect him from inferiority feelings, the student acts in a manner that betrays these feelings. He degrades his fellow students, shows sensitivity in his social relationships, thinks too highly of himself, withdraws from participation, becomes easily angry when threatened, overreacts to criticism, blatantly denies that he has any weaknesses, and becomes unduly aggressive in situations which do not require such behavior.

When one's childhood feelings of insecurity and inferiority, with their natural consequences of feelings of personal weaknesses, have not been properly resolved and compensated for, by the time that he becomes an adolescent, they may have some kind of ill effect on the student's functioning in college. However, college and society do provide ways by which the student can relieve himself of these feelings. He can compensate by excelling within the limits of his abilities. But, should he feel that this cannot be easily accomplished, there may be deeper emotional factors which prevent him from making full use of his talents. Lack of adequate identity and goals, unresolved conflicts with parents or with vocational choice, and a host of other factors may be present. If a student is successful but still feels inferior, then the real reason comes from within himself; and if such feelings annoy him excessively, he may need to seek professional assistance.

As long as the student is able to feel that he belongs somewhere, and that he can offer to society just as much as anyone with the same capabilities, he will not experience inferiority feelings strong enough to give him discomfort. He can develop a sense of belonging within himself by behaving toward other people in a way that benefits them, thereby becoming important to them. Thus, as he becomes a significant figure in their lives, he is made to feel accepted by them. Other people will approve of and accept a student to the extent that his behavior is conducive to their welfare. Under these circumstances, the student is bound to feel significant, and to complain less of meaninglessness and emptiness in his life. Guided by realistic values, and orienting his energies toward society's welfare, the student can overcome his feelings of inferiority.

## The Need for Identity and Meaning

Throughout the ages of the history of man, there has been

a typical struggle in every human being, particularly during his adolescent and early adult years, to find himself, to determine in his own mind the kind of person he wants to be. He looks for an ideology which will be more clear to him, one that will help to advance his emotional growth, and bring him into a closer harmony with other people. Such an individual desires to know, further, how he fits into the pattern of society, what kind of role he is going to adopt, and what there will be about him that will make him who and what he is, that will distinguish him from other people.

This activity is often referred to as the search for one's *identity*. It may begin in high school and extend into the college years where it usually becomes more pronounced. But then it is resolved as the student finds meaning in his existence, develops a sense of independence, and acquires a satisfying identity as an adult with a profession, a family, a religion, and a purpose in life. For a student not to have already experienced or be currently undergoing some kind of identity problem is a rare phenomenon. On the other hand, a few students do suffer from lack of identity to such a degree that they cannot accomplish very much in college or find success. Lack of identity in the student may be aggravated and prolonged by an unstable environment, and by the student's inability to make the proper choices for himself.

The reason the concept of identity today is quite important for the college student is that the emergence of the democratic way of life places greater emphasis on individual choice and freedom in social, vocational, religious, and many other facets of life. A century ago, the roles of each sex were more definite; the adolescent, more or less, knew what he should do in life and what he wanted to achieve for himself. Unless he is prepared, today's male student may be confused by his many roles and choices. The same is true for the female student, although several decades ago her major role in life was to marry and have children. Now, the student must concern himself with making a choice and committing himself to it. However, before he does, he must become familiar with the alternatives, and this necessitates more time, thus prolonging his struggle for identity.

The college student who is in the process of becoming a

mature adult must go through this period of struggle, in order to define himself. He often achieves this by giving up behavior characteristic of childhood, and by getting others to accept what he wants himself to be. He wants to match his present concept of himself with what he desires to become in terms of the personal qualities that his milieu recognizes and esteems. He often realizes that he is in the process of becoming something, but he may not be too sure what it may be. He wants to feel that what is taking place currently in his life will have some meaning in terms of what he expects to become. What frequently happens is that he plays different roles which eventually become integrated with himself, and he ends up by retaining those roles that are consistent with his abilities, and by rejecting those that are incompatible. Thus, he becomes more concrete and definite about himself, his work, his relations to other people, and his goals in life.

The concept of self-identity is a very important one for the college student. By the term *identity* is meant the way in which the student is different from everybody else, and what there is about him that makes him what he is. As the student becomes aware of his selfhood, he begins to recognize his personal qualities and to feel less confused about the functions and the roles that are typically assigned to his age group. The lack of self-identity in the student means that he does not know what he should be, and what he should do in life. Furthermore, he is not able to picture himself in the future doing things that are satisfying to himself, unless he can experience a concise awareness of who he is, what his goals are, and what his conduct should be. Below is an example of an identity problem:

A female student complained of not having any clear-cut, satisfying identification. She stated, "I don't know who I am." By this she meant that she had no clear idea of her abilities and where they fit in the scheme of things. She did not have trustworthy convictions about anything, she felt aimless and just drifting, and she did not experience the satisfaction of living her own life, with her own ideals. She talked about having to agree totally with people, and of not wanting to hurt their feelings, or to cause a disturbance. She mentioned having painful indecisions, and a need to accept the value system of whatever person she is with at the time. "I am what other people want me to be," she said. She had no convictions about a way of life, and she considered herself "wishy-washy." She mentioned further that she frequently entertained people by her stupid remarks when she had no intention of being funny. Although she laughed along with others at some of her own remarks, deep down her feelings were hurt. She also felt that no one took her seriously when she had some serious things to say.

Group therapy helped this girl establish a framework of values and goals which brought meaning and solidification to her life. By realizing that other students in her group experienced similar feelings, and that with sufficient time and effort she could arrive at some ground for action in her life, she began to formulate in her own mind what her goals and values ought to be. The finding of an identity is not a very difficult process. The fact is that some students are fortunate enough to acquire or develop it sooner than others. Certainly, some factors in the late development of identity may stem from childhood. However, if the student is given the proper opportunity by exchanging his ideas, feelings, and experiences with others, he is, sooner or later, bound to arrive at his own conclusions about the whole idea of life, how he should live it, and what his actions should be.

By way of analogy, the student can think of an object being projected on a screen but out of focus. It appears indefinite, blurred, diffused; he is unable to recognize, define, and clarify the object because he cannot distinguish its properties. The same can be applied to the adolescent's feelings of selfhood. He cannot put himself into "focus" and recognize his identity; in his own mind he seems to be a mass of things; he cannot pinpoint anything concrete about himself. It must be remembered that this condition is normal and typical of a great number of students. The lack of identity becomes a real problem when the student requires an unusually long time to achieve it. Meanwhile, as his behavior becomes aimless, he may easily develop anxiety or depression. The result is often to seek treatment for these symptoms alone, while being unaware of the real problem, his lack of self-identity.

Another facet of the identity problem is shown by the student's concern with how he should deal with, and what his attitude should be toward, the opposite sex. Often, a male student has difficulty in this area because he feels uncomfortable about his apparent lack of desirable masculine characteristics. As a result, such a student may relinquish heterosexual social relationships in favor of excelling academically. By doing this, he can hide his poor feelings of himself behind scholastic achievement. The girl, on the other hand, is expected to win the approval of the male through social charm and affability, without becoming overbearing or seductive. The male is expected to be aggressive, but not to the degree where the female feels threatened by him. Both sexes feel a concern about their sexual impulses, and how to defend against them. The greater their self-confidence about their sexual identity, the more will be their sense of security and self-control in their relationships with the opposite sex.

Identity begins with sexual differentiation and with the student's attitude toward his own body. If what he depicts as ideal in terms of masculinity or femininity conforms to what he or she happens to be in reality, then self-identity becomes stronger. The student is able to play the role linked to his sex, and to choose a profession which is consistent with his self-identity. Likewise, the more the student is convinced of his abilities, goals, interests and status in life, the more he is likely to know who he is. If he has little difficulty defining himself, he will work with the conviction that he will achieve the things that are consistent with his image of himself. By knowing who and what he is, he becomes better able to act his own real role, and he knows what his place should be as he relates himself to other people.

If the student feels that he has deficiencies in his physical identity, his body-concept can become distorted, a condition which can develop many kinds of friction as he relates to other members of his group. The male student may become assertive and outgoing in order to assure himself of his masculinity or he may become withdrawn, shy, and defensive. The female who feels that she lacks physically feminine traits may either try to be overly sweet and pleasing, or may pretend she has no real need for males, and that they do not impress her.

The search for identity is often expressed by the student's typical comments, such as, "I feel depressed, aimless, and lonesome because everything just skirts on the outside, and there's no meaning to anything." "I haven't the foggiest idea of what I am: I just exist; I feel like a blob of protoplasm, like a nothingism." These thoughts indicate that the student wants to feel that he has a place in the world; that he is struggling for something but does not know exactly what it should be. Others are excessively sensitive to the inconsistencies and injustices in the world and try to struggle with philosophical concepts, often as a need to find an answer for the reason why something should or should not be done. Following is an essay by a student in which he typically depicts his struggle to find something meaningful in his life.

I have become so entangled in the morass of the absurdity of my own existence, that I feel as if trapped in some great inimical vise—a vise from which an act of extrication itself would only result in a freedom which I would be unable to bear. It seems to me apparent that I have come to an end of "meaning" and "sense," and as a result, I no longer feel that I possess any integrity of Being. I loath going to bed and sometimes I never do. I do this because I hate the thought of having to confront tomorrow. I seem to be awaiting some great cataclysmic event about whose nature I have not the slightest idea. I just seem to know that it is coming. For this reason, I sometimes think I am on the brink of insanity. On the other hand, I also suspect, more often than not, that I want to be insane. Another distressing fact: I claim to be an agnostic and I *used* to be able to argue my point most elegantly—now I cannot. Perhaps this indicates that I either believe in God or that I am afraid that he *really* does not exist. For the sake of my façade, I hope that neither case is true. I am sick and tired of chasing after constructions and finding them, without exception, in a bizarre tangle of mockery. I cannot accept the world without first attaining to absolute certainty, and I cannot be certain without first accepting the world. So many times I have constructed essential structures in which I have placed a certain measure of faith. At present I question as to whether or not these essential structures are actually consistent with reality, or if they exist only as a self-interpretation of my mind disguised as metaphysics or, better still, as a metaphysical sickness.

Nearly every student who reads the above passages will readily identify these feelings in himself and say, "That's me, all right." The next probable step for him is to ask what he should do about this problem now that he has formed in his mind a clear picture of it. The anguish that the student experiences during the period of his identity confusion cannot be readily lifted or diminished; it must take its normal time. The time it takes for the resolution of the identity problem will be different for each student. As an analogy, let us take the process of digestion. Physiologically, it requires a few hours for food to digest; the time is necessary on account of the nature of this process, and it usually cannot be reduced to a matter of a few minutes. The same criterion applies for the establishment of identity. Neither can the student force himself, or be taught what identity he should have, since its formation involves, more or less, a natural course. However, the student's conscious efforts in the proper direction, as he experiments with different roles and as he becomes acquainted with persons who have already established their own identity, can be an enormous advantage to him.

Along with personal elements, sociological factors are often responsible for the creation of an identity problem in the college student. With the growth of industry, the population has become more urbanized. The closeness of the rural neighborhood and particularly of the family units has relatively disappeared with the growth of urbanization. Family life has become more distant, and the coherence of the family unit has become weaker. City life is generally anonymous and impersonal, and lacks the friendliness and warmth found in rural communities. These characteristics can create a feeling of emptiness in one's life, and the individual tends to lose his personal identity. Many of these social characteristics may be found in the college environment. The student frequently does not know what his goal in life is, what meaning is contained in living, or what constitutes happiness. Finally, another social factor is the mass media of communication which tend to bring closer the world conflicts and crises to the individual.

The student who lacks intimate personal communication with others has a tendency to isolate himself and become involved with impersonal situations; when life's problems or the demands of college become too severe, he has no one to help him or guide him properly. Also, the student who comes from a closely knit family background but who has always been a socially withdrawn person and emotionally close to his parents, may have a greater identity problem in college than the student who has been a strong social participant and a more or less independent person. Neither extreme closeness and emotional involvement, nor aloofness and distance from parents or any person is a desirable characteristic, for neither contributes to the early establishment of personal identity.

During the period of crisis in his search for a meaningful identity, the student's thoughts, feelings, and actions are not well coordinated with a clear goal. He may assume and experiment with different goals for short periods of time, he may tend to waver between different people's opinions, and he may have no clear idea of where he is heading. He is actually looking for a purpose for himself, but he does not know what it should be. As a solution for his dilemma, he may either entertain grandiose daydreams or he may go to the opposite end of the scale and think too little of himself, or he can vacillate between these two opposing points. The realistic solution is, ultimately, to find and establish a satisfying midpoint. The student has to face and accept the facts about himself, and by doing this, he will eventually face his goals and purposes. The void created by the lack of identity can sometimes be fulfilled by a true religious experience, an identification with the values and beliefs of a religious faith.

## Religion and Values

Another important aspect in the study of human behavior is the student's religious experiences and his scheme of values in general. Psychologists and anthropologists often indicate that the survival of a society depends largely upon the ultimate values and religious attitudes of its individual members. One's values, which have been formed through personal and social experiences, form his ultimate ideals and are of utmost worth to him. Religious beliefs and ethical values help to maintain one's strength and give meaning to his existence. Consequently, it is not uncommon to find students whose religious convictions are well integrated with the rest of their personality able to withstand the adversities of life much more easily than those who have not integrated any religious values at all.

There is no doubt that healthy religious convictions strengthen the whole family and the marriage bond. On the other hand, there are many students who profess and strongly adhere to their religious traditions, but who are very unhappy in their lives and uncertain about themselves. It may be that the religious attitudes in these persons are not genuinely integrated with their total personality; these students merely go through religious rituals and observances to avoid rejection by those they esteem and value. Another frequent phenomenon among students is the tendency to express hostility and rebelliousness toward anything religious. In many cases, their reaction to religion serves as a symbolic substitute for something else that is actually the real source of their hostility. In most instances, these students have a tendency to recover their religious convictions as they become older; others remain the same throughout their lives. Some students change from the faith of their parents to one of their own choice. Since parents represent authority, it is natural that children indirectly rebel against them by espousing a religion other than their parents'. It is also true that not all changes in religious beliefs constitute rebellion against parents. It is not surprising to find many students returning to their parents' religion after the adolescent rebellion has otherwise been resolved or subsided.

A genuine interest in religion serves to counterbalance the materialistic pursuits of daily life. The college student has mental, emotional, and spiritual components in his personality which can hardly be ignored if the aim of a college education is to sustain the growth of his total personality. The college student cannot live apart from the beliefs and ideals that his society condones and maintains; nor can he ignore its values and aims. Happiness and a feeling of well-being in the student are derived not only from the fulfillment of his needs and drives, but also from the extent to which he has been able to attain such religious ideals and values as were shown to be significant for his society, and to make them part of his own self. The college student who is expected to make an emotional and intellectual adaptation would be misleading himself to believe that these two objectives are the only goals for him. These happen to be immediate goals; religion, on the other hand, provides the ultimate goals which are just as necessary in the total picture of a human being.

There is no person who does not admit the necessity of a guide for living, a plan of operation, or a philosophy of life. What we mean is that the mature and well-adjusted person has some idea of the reason for his being, and his actions and knowledge serve to that end. A philosophy of living gives meaning to one's conduct and makes it consistent with the values that his philosophy espouses. The college student normally goes through a period of skepticism and doubt, but eventually he begins to integrate into his personality the values and attitudes toward life which are the time-tested products of the wisdom of his society. In other words, he has found that what is already available to him is the most useful and enduring philosophy of living. However, it must also be pointed out that religion *alone* does not solve all the student's emotional problems. Religion complements, but does not substitute for, treatment of the student's psychological difficulties.

It must be emphasized that religion may provide an excellent guide to a philosophy of living, a code of conduct for the basic issues and most sensitive phases of life, and a clue to the ultimate purpose for one's existence. Religion also furnishes a hierarchy of values, so that the student can make the best decision should there be a conflict of choices. It is important for the student to be aware of this, from early life, so that he can have available a framework or a blue-print, so to speak, from which he can make judgments on ethical, social, and vocational matters. Although some values are fundamental and are considered as basic, there are many others which can vary from person to person, and can be flexible along with the current needs, as long as the basic values are not violated or contradicted.

Some students have difficulty accepting their current way of living. The primary reason for this difficulty may be that they are not mature enough to accept all the responsibilities for their conduct, in terms of the philosophy of life which was taught to them. Others accept a philosophy of living on a logical basis alone and are reluctant to put it to use because, according to their thinking, it implies conformity to a pre-established way of behaving. These students derive some temporary gratification from the feeling that non-conformity makes them appear superior and "strong." Such naive attitudes are not conducive to emotional adjustment in college and can cause further repercussions on the student's academic performance. At the same time, to have flexible values is just as important, as long as the basic ones are properly interpreted and the distinction is made between primary and secondary values. The less important values can differ in every person, provided they do not contradict the basic ones. Once the basic values have been established and accepted, the secondary ones will eventually fall into their proper perspective. Religion can provide basic values to the student who is willing to accept them.

When a student has personal conflicts, he may develop a distorted attitude toward religion. He can be "religious" from the external point of view, that is, a student can call himself religious on the basis that he goes through the rubrics, the mechanics of religious services, but with little faith in the fundamental tenets of his religion. Or, he can tenaciously hold on to religious beliefs simply because they offer him prestige, status, and a screen for his transgressions. Obviously, the student with this attitude will not be too happy with himself, nor with his religion because he has not fully understood it; as a result he easily finds faults with it. An honest religious experience does not tear apart the student or make him feel depressed and unworthy of himself. It creates a sense of coordination between him and his environment, and he is better able to deal with difficult life situations more effectively and with less personal discomfort.

A healthy orientation of religious values enables the student to accept his shortcomings with greater ease. Every student recognizes undesirable traits in himself, traits which he is able to keep under control most of the time. Disorderliness, procrastination, anger, envy, indolence, etc., are universal experiences which are not readily shown because our society disapproves of them, and the basic values and positive attitudes in the student's personality keep them under control. It would be a mistake for one to attempt to eradicate these feelings described above. Rather, he must learn the ability to keep these self-defeating feelings in check. It would be unreasonable to expect a student with an excellent record not to become angry after receiving a D grade, or to be turned down for a date with someone he particularly likes and not feel disappointed. But if anger and disappointment become too visibly evident over a long period of time, he may be overreacting to stress. Strong religious values can help the student keep his impulses under control.

The student can also reflect on his own experiences and find meaning for his activities and pursuits if he looks upon himself as belonging to a larger *design*, which may even be beyond his comprehension. Such reflections may predispose him to devotion and a sense of reverence and duty toward *creation* and the *universe*. These feelings and thoughts are often expressed directly through religion and they give a sense of direction to one's activities, and make living seem worthwhile. Many students have found contentment and meaning in being able to meditate and to reflect upon themselves. However, some students who in college are encouraged to think for themselves and to question popular beliefs, may be tempted to challenge their religious beliefs and values logically. Religious values are not meant to be under the scrutiny of logic, but they are accepted on the basis of faith.

*Faith* in himself and in a plan greater than himself, can have an enormous effect upon the unhappy and tormented student. As he enters college, he will ultimately have to make decisions and plans which will affect his whole life. Despite his personal abilities, financial means, educational opportunities, etc., he may not necessarily be able to achieve his goals without the faith and conviction that he will succeed. Many persons are unaware of its presence and take faith for granted. For example, if one boards a plane, he has faith that the captain knows how to navigate the craft. This fact is assumed and never questioned. Likewise, having faith and hope that he will succeed in college can sustain the student in times of difficulty.

This psychological phenomenon of faith can have the same effect when applied to the existence of an Omnipotent Being, higher than the student himself. As he identifies himself with this Supreme Being, he derives support and feels less inferior. He, thus, can feel that he is here for a purpose, and he feels that his existence has meaning. Religion provides security for the student, and a code of ethics. He has little difficulty deciding what is right or wrong. The student whose religious convictions are strong feels enlightened as he shares the stresses and burdens of everyday life with his Creator.

### Purposefulness and Goals

Although religion enhances the student's self-identity, his use of purposeful activities that guide him toward realistic goals plays a significant role in the formation of his identity. Many psychologists believe that human behavior is goal-directed. There is no human activity that is not associated with some kind of objective. Goals that are meaningful to the student motivate him to apply himself; they give him a feeling of purpose in the things he does. When the student works without being able to visualize a goal, he will eventually become disinterested, listless, unhappy, and sometimes anxious and depressed. He feels that everything is meaningless; he sees no point in taking courses and earning grades if they will mean nothing to him at the end. Some students do not even see the value of a college education, unless it will serve them a real purpose.

The student would normally feel "lost" and his life would be devoid of meaning if he did not know where his activities were leading him or what his ultimate personal and academic objectives were. Such feelings may be felt even by a person who has some perspective and objective in life. When we observe a play, for example, we become frustrated and confused when some parts of the play do not seem to fit; but as we reach the end, the minor parts attain a proper perspective when the final act is played. Likewise, the student's activities and studies in college are pulled together and make sense when viewed in the light of the final event toward which they lead: graduation.

By goal we mean a future event which propels the student to act and strive in the present time, and the end-result of this activity is looked upon by the student as being rewarding and beneficial to him. Behavior leading toward a goal can be changed when the goal has been altered, since behavior in general normally leads to some goal. Hence, if behavior is unacceptable, it can be averted if its goal is altered. The student with healthy and realistic goals is more apt to be motivated to succeed, and to find interest in his work. Also, he is able to postpone the satisfaction of immediate needs (money, marriage) for the sake of higher aims which will give him a feeling of recognition and fulfillment later.

The student's current behavior cannot be explained totally from his past experiences. If this were true, then a great number of students would be suffering from some type of emotional disturbance, and many would not consider trying to sustain themselves in college pursuing academic goals. There is no student who has not experienced an unfortunate or an unpleasant event sometime during the span of his lifetime. In most cases, such instances can be looked upon with a healthy attitude, and can challenge the student to overcome past unpleasant experiences. Many successful students may ignore the unpleasant aspects of their lives. It is what *use* the student makes of the past that is important, rather than making it responsible for his present situation. It sounds more plausible to say that someone was rejected or unloved to justify academic failure than to say that his current failure is due to his own inability or to his lack of interest and goals.

Experience has shown that the student's behavior cannot be predicted simply by knowing the degree of intelligence alone, or by knowing the kind of childhood he lived. He may act independently of these two factors, either by using his weakness as a challenge to success, or by conveniently using his weaknesses to justify his current failure. There are just as many students who do very well academically despite their personal problems, as those who fail because of their current problems. It is up to the student as to what attitude he is going to use, and what approach he is going to adopt toward his difficulties. The student's goals (optimistic or pessimistic) will influence his present behavior. He will normally act in the present according to what he can expect from the future.

Another tendency in the somewhat sophisticated college student is to blame his problems on reasons which are unconscious to him. Although a great deal of the student's behavior is beyond his immediate awareness, he cannot conclude that the unconscious segment of his personality is entirely responsible for all his activities. It would be more practical for the college student to concentrate on and deal with his problems by considering them first as conscious factors of his personality which can thus be dealt with more effectively. No matter how much of his behavior in college the student is unable to understand, there is no need to attach an element of magic or mystery to his "unconscious." For many students, the belief that behavior in college is caused by unconscious elements is simply a means to avoid their real problem. It would be much better for them to say that they do not understand their behavior in relation to the way they look upon their future and to their lack of goals.

Experience indicates that the student's present attitudes and feelings depend on the promises of the future and on the certainty of rewards that his present studies will give him. The student's expectations of future gains combine with the current situational stress to influence him and make him feel the way he does. The student who comes to the campus to pursue an academic career is, in nearly all cases, pretty much convinced that he is capable of achieving the goals that he is determined to undertake.

## Personality Types in College Students

Broadly speaking, adolescent college students exhibit *four* general types of personality. These types are determined according to the way the student meets the challenges of higher education, and how he adjusts to campus life. Every normal student has the characteristics of one or of all types, and in varying degrees. As he recognizes them in himself he can gain some general notions on how to go about modifying them. These categories are *descriptive* of the student, and they reflect the manner in which he copes with the stress of academic work. They also provide an indication about both the type of his upbringing which molded his personality, and the type of relationship which exists between himself and others.

The *first* type is the student who becomes involved in many projects without being able to contribute fully to and complete any one of them. He expresses his emotions quite readily, he states his opinion at the drop of a hat, and his energies are often spent in areas that have little to do with academic work. He may, otherwise, be very popular, show interest in other people, and deal effectively with various issues in life. The paradox is that he can control everyone else, but he cannot discipline himself with respect to his duties as a college student. It is not uncommon for this type of student to have a deep feeling that he can succeed if he really tries, or that he is some sort of a genius whom the world does not yet appreciate. Compensating for academic failure by excelling in extra-curricular activities is a more justifiable excuse than to admit that the latter is the cause of the former.

Students exhibiting these characteristics eventually learn from their mistakes and become better students, although they have, unnecessarily, wasted time and energy in college with little compensation. Such students are somewhat immature toward college work, and normally outgrow these features as the reality of college begins to catch up with them. One cannot remain for long in college, if his main reasons for being there are other than doing academic work. In most instances, these students eventually are compelled to give up their other activities in favor of becoming more productive scholastically; otherwise, they would have to drop out of college. Those students who fail because they have exaggerated characteristics of this type should re-examine their motivation for being in college.

The *second* type is the student who achieves excellent academic work, who is able to get things done in a systematic way and whose behavior is generally over-controlled. He is considered as the "intellectual" type who does not make friends easily, and who prefers to remain alone studying or listening to records rather than being in the company of other students and sharing his interests with them. His speech, thinking, and actions are quite rigid. At times he may express hostility through cynicism or intellectually challenging questions in the class room. He is generally considered as socially impoverished.

This type of student, in most cases, does not pose any great difficulty in his college adjustment. In fact, he may be quite appealing intellectually to the academic staff, and, since he is usually a good student, his personality traits almost go unnoticed; he is accepted for what he is, and he gives no one any difficulty. The only problem that he may have would be in the choice of friends, and in his choice of a place to work. But most such persons are able to overcome these impediments, since they are normally capable persons. Finally, some students of this type may eventually learn to exude emotion, and to show warmth and spontaneity when the conditions call for such feelings.

The *third* category includes the type of student who fails in college because he is constantly ill. This student, in order to gain sympathy and attention, is preoccupied with minor illnesses, and imagines such diseases as cancer and heart trouble. He goes to the college health department at the appearance of the slightest symptom, and looks for someone to sympathize with him. Hostility and resentment toward college or parents, disinterest in his chosen vocation or curriculum, and lack of motivation for academic work are some of the more frequent reasons for such behavior. By proving the existence of an illness, he can be absolved from responsibility and failure. He also may try to gain attention and sympathy from his professors, by constantly talking about his helplessness and inabilities. Although this type of student is not very common, it is worth discussing because such students do present a problem to the college authorities.

The reason for this kind of behavior is often unknown, at least to the student; he may have difficulty responding to insight, and he may fail altogether to respond to reassurances. In such cases, health authorities are helpless, for the student accepts very little from anyone because he considers such help either insufficient or false. Should his real problem consist of a lasting resentment toward those he needs and depends upon, he may sense a deep gratification for being in a position where no one can really do anything for him. Instead of showing motivation that comes from within himself, he wants assistance to reach him from the outside. "Please, do something" is often his plea and attitude. No one can really do much for such a student, unless he begins to understand the emotional basis for his unnecessary helplessness and his attention getting devices. Frequently, administrative pressure that his college attendance will be contingent upon accepting the recommendations of the college health authorities is quite effective.

In the *fourth* category is the student who is never satisfied with the grades he earns in college, no matter how high they are, nor is he ever satisfied with his social successes. He is concerned with the impression he is making on others, and he does not cooperate genuinely with his fellow students unless there is a guarantee that he will benefit from such a venture. He wants to be recognized and appreciated, and because his close associates find it difficult to tolerate his selfish needs, he ultimately alienates them. He expects everyone to show esteem and admiration toward him. His actions are aimed at being a "show-off," rather than at achieving realistic ambitions and striving in proportion to his ability. In social organizations and group activities, he may demand that others follow his admonitions and become angry if they ignore him; in class, he may challenge the instructor on a relatively minor point.

Such students feel inferior and are fundamentally insecure; yet, they may not be aware of their inferiority feelings. These feelings can be inferred from the way the student acts and feels about himself. He tries to elevate himself by becoming critical of others, and fails to recognize any worth in those who happen to be successful. In many of his efforts to excel, he excludes others from consideration, his own goals being of primary importance. Usually, such a student will show perceptible changes in his behavior, as he gradually becomes aware of the fact that his past behavior is not really helpful in the long run, and there are ways of behaving that are more pleasant and beneficial to him. If he feels comfortable with himself and of value to others, and if he experiences an inner sense of security that he has a proper place and belongs in the campus society, he need not act in this way.

The student with exaggerated features of this type, which interfere with his college work and social interaction, frequently requires a basic reorientation to life. He needs to understand himself first, before there can be any change in his approach to others. He has to accept the idea that unrealistic demands and criticisms directed at others reveal his own weaknesses. Not only must he accept this idea intellectually, but he also has to feel this way. Once he looks at himself realistically and admits that such unacceptable behavior is used to conceal factors about himself that he does not want to face, he is making the first step toward a better adaptation. The real challenge for this type of student is to see and accept himself as being on an equal basis with others, and to concede that his own virtues and shortcomings are already found in other persons. However, if the characteristics of this type of student are rigid and persistent, professional assistance may be to his advantage.

Although students who exhibit these personality types are not necessarily poorly adjusted, an exaggeration of these types may create academic and adjustment difficulties. After the student has read and become familiar with these types, he normally can expect to identify a few of them in himself. If he is not currently experiencing any significant problem, he can ignore these characteristics. If he has found some features in himself, he can search for others with similar characteristics who happen to be successful, and discover how they found success despite the type of person they happen to be. Finally, if he realizes that he is overwhelmed with many of these features of one or more types, and at the same time he is experiencing academic or social problems, then he can consult the proper mental health personnel. The sooner he begins, the easier it will be for him to modify his behavior.

# 3

## AREAS OF MALADJUSTMENT IN COLLEGE

Because the student's primary concern in college is to perform well scholastically and to obtain a degree, the most frequent complaint of college students is their lack of ability to study effectively. However, there is usually a combination of many factors, personal and social, which affect the student's academic performance. This section will cover the major areas with which most students have concerned or will concern themselves, in one way or another, during their college career.

### The Inability to Study

A considerable number of students who seek assistance from health services or psychological and counseling agencies on campus complain of an inability to study, concentrate, or "get organized" in their work. Many of these students suffer in this area because they have not learned to utilize the proper study techniques; others simply do not take college work seriously. At the end of the semester, when there is little time left for learning new material, they become concerned. The result is that the student becomes tense and anxious and develops physical symptoms which he hopes will excuse him from examinations. It is possible that the anxious student who cannot study may have a problem not directly connected with the course material he is studying.

The student should remember that periodic bouts of laziness and tiredness are normal and acceptable, and do not necessarily constitute a problem for the student. He usually finds time later to study when he feels better motivated, and he is seldom behind in his studies. However, one of the common problems of adolescence and young adulthood is a prolonged indifference toward doing academic work. This condition may be manifested by lethargy and sluggishness. The student withdraws from participation. He is constantly sleepy and tired; he daydreams of success, and he "just can't get started." Below is a typical case of such a student who sought assistance for his inability to study. He verbalized his problem as follows:

> "I have no control over my fate and I am avoiding life. I like doing things that are easy, like playing cards. My mind is just lazy—not fresh. I just sit around and do nothing. I can't get rooted and I can't discipline myself. My mind stops; I can't think, I can't cure myself of my inhibitions, of my exaggerated tendency to worry about something until it actually occurs. I'm just a pessimist; I daydream and fall into trances. A sort of aphasia seems to come over me when I am in a situation where I should say something. I'm just a spectator of life—not really participating, but just existing—not going forward, not creating but just waiting to see what the next day will bring. I study word by word; so, I take dexedrine to keep my eyes glued to the book."

Most students such as this one who are dissatisfied with their scholastic performance are not achieving grades equivalent to their intellectual ability. While many of them may have a legitimate emotional problem which interferes with their academic performance, some have been producing below their potential merely because of laziness and a "don't care" attitude. Their reason for being in college is vague, or is based on the idea that attending college is the best thing for them to do at the present time. This is not a strong enough justification for attending college, for activity without some personal meaning behind it is not expected to be satisfying to the student.

The student who, despite his above-average ability, cannot study or concentrate, or who sleeps during the day and studies at night without being able to accomplish very much shows an obvious tendency to evade the tasks to which he has committed himself, or is pursuing them superficially. Here we see some kind of frustration which can be identified when he seeks assistance. The student feels perplexed when he cannot reach an aim, although consciously he may desire this particular goal. Of course, there is a difference between not wanting to do college work from lack of interest, and not being able to accomplish it despite the stated willingness. The latter behavior suggests that there are negative feelings of which the student is not aware that are holding him back. Once they are brought out into the open, discussed with a counselor, and reappraised, their effect more or less diminishes.

A few notions should be expressed concerning the student's sleeping habits, since in many the patterns of sleep seem to vary to such a large degree that sometimes they become totally reversed. The student who cannot awaken in the morning is most likely the one who has gone late to bed. He can learn to study in a regular, quiet place during the day and evening and to sleep at night. Otherwise, he will be sleepy during his class attendance. If the student receives adequate sleep during the night, he should not have to use stimulants and to cram before exams. Should he continue to fall asleep during the day, despite a full night's sleep, then other factors may be present (physical or psychological) which he can investigate with a physician and a counselor.

Almost everyone has the ability to study and concentrate if there are no distractions, if the material is interesting, if he has had adequate sleep and feels physically healthy, and above all, if the level of motivation is high. Inability to concentrate is often related to worrying either about things that are unrelated to studies (girlfriends, parents, job), or about whether the student will be able to learn enough to do well in his examinations. Sometimes the reasons for being unable to study may be outside the student's awareness (hostility towards parents, basic insecurity, etc.). If he feels unable to make the desired changes in himself or the environment so as to be able to study and absorb the material, the student can be assured that there are helpful people whom he can consult.

One way for the student to cope with his inability to study is to look for causes in his immediate environment. Taking courses randomly without having in mind definite scholastic goals, and having no strong interest in any particular field are common and obvious causes. Other factors can play important roles, such as undue pressure from parents to excel regardless of the student's ability to do college work, concern over parents and other family members who have domestic problems, an unresolved conflict with a member of the opposite sex, undesirable study conditions, and a host of other reasons. The ones just mentioned seem to be the most prevalent of those that come to the attention of mental hygienists who work with students' problems. In many cases, however, the real reason may not be as obvious as stated above, but may come from more subtle factors in the student's personality of which he is not aware.

The student's inability to study can first be managed by the manipulation of his environment. Changing his curriculum, taking aptitude tests to determine his ability to do the work in which he has difficulty, and eliminating other pressures that may be interfering are a few first steps that can be taken. If the reason for a student's lack of interest can be focused on a specific condition, then recovery can be expected to be easy; if his inability to concentrate and to indicate interest has lingered for a long period of time, recovery may be more difficult. Even good students may, occasionally, lose interest in their academic work for a short period of time, only to resume their responsibilities again. In these situations, of course, psychologic or psychiatric consultation is not always necessary; however, it would be necessary if the student's apathy towards his studies is prolonged.

Frequently, the real reason for the lack of stamina and enthusiasm in fulfilling his academic requirements lies in deeper psychological factors which remain unknown to the student. Fear of involvement because of the possibility of failure can make the student unable to come to grips with his work. As already stated, when the student does not feel able to perform a given task, he tries to avoid loss of self-esteem and disgrace by evading his duties. His feeling of lethargy and inertia and his aversion to activity come on automatically as a face saving device. By not doing anything, he is less likely to be hurt, and he encourages others to rescue him by being helpless. The student's "lack of energy" is often a defense against his felt personal weaknesses. Finally, inability to study can stem from the need for attention, from lack of self-identity, from hostility against some aspect of education, and it may even stem from guilt and depression. The student can be totally unaware of these reasons. Nevertheless, the student should seek assistance if his apathy toward his studies becomes persistent.

There have been instances when the inability to study is the result of the student's wrong motivation for college. The desire to specialize in a particular field because of the money or prestige involved, or because of competition with a parent or an older sibling in the family, rather than having a real *interest* in the field, are typical examples. In many cases, these students feel they will be unaccepted and "left out" if they do not, at least, pretend to be aiming at academic objectives for which they may not be fully qualified. Although a few such students do succeed, despite their inadequate reasons for being in college, many others are forced to change into another field compatible with their real interests.

Lack of encouragement and a feeling of personal inadequacy which was instilled in the student by his parents during his earlier years in school by comparing him with his brighter peers, may make studying more difficult for him. Such comparisons can form in the student a very poor concept of himself, and he may act according to these unfavorable comparisons; he may expect low grades and he accepts them as indications of what he is really worth. Such a student may never really take a strong interest in his courses, and he may be wasting his talents simply because he is convinced that his mental capacity is only average or lower. Other students may resent their parents, and conveniently punish them by failing in school. Of course, it is not always an act of revenge against the parents if the student fails unless the parents are involved by way of rejecting, punishing, or setting up high expectations from the student. With his underachievement he humiliates his parents by "letting them down."

Every college and university is faced with the request from a few students who wish to take a leave of absence or to drop out of school for a semester or a year in order to "mature" and "get some experience from life" so that they will be able to meet the college requirements. Many of these students have a high scholastic aptitude, and had been good students in high school. Their decision to leave college for a while may be advisable, as in certain cases where strong emotional dependency, immaturity, and high expectations from parents are evident. For others, leaving college may be unnecessary if the reason is to "just take it easy for a while and enjoy life while you're young." These students do not realize that eventually they will have to return to where they left off.

The college student should have an idea of why he is in college; otherwise, his studies will have no meaning for him. Should the student have reasonable goals but still find himself unable to study effectively, he should rule out the possibility of physical factors (poor vision, vitamin deficiency). The next step is for the otherwise well-motivated and physically healthy student to examine his study habits. A slow reading rate, poor vocabulary, disorganized study schedule, inability to memorize the landmarks of an assignment and to take notes and prepare for examination are a few of the areas which should be investigated. Any effort to improve an area in which the student is deficient should come mainly from himself. There is no doubt that attending college is a period of stress for the student, but the student should realize that college, like any ordinary job, requires the necessary time and the use of appropriate energy; otherwise, the results will be unsatisfactory.

Stress is a difficult concept to define; what may constitute stress for one student may not be so for another. Students tolerate stress in different ways. Consequently, there is no reason to feel that all students should react identically to the same problem. Neither should they compare each other, for each student, although he may be similar to others in many ways, he also has characteristics which can hardly be duplicated. Furthermore, he can make good use of his unique abilities once he has recognized them. If he has demonstrated interest and excellence in a particular vocational area, or has taken interest and aptitude tests that are administered and interpreted by a psychologist, he can match his abilities with his academic load.

Stress for the student of above-average intelligence can be

quite beneficial, because it serves as a challenge and it motivates him to make use of his capabilities. If college does not stimulate him, he can easily become disappointed and withdraw from genuine participation or find some other activity which is entirely different from his college tasks. Stress in college usually arises from the meeting of deadlines, parents' expectations, the making of decisions, and the having to accomplish college work which is beyond his capacity. Stress also can originate from within the student's personality; strong feelings of inferiority, guilt from failures, conflicts over choices can all inhibit the student as he copes with his environment.

The inability to study is often blamed on distractions in the student's environment. But there are instances when the student cannot study, even in quiet conditions, or when he studies perfectly well in noisier conditions. What is more important is the student's attitude towards these conditions, and his feelings about himself. When he is unhappy and angry about his performance, or is ridden by internal conflicts, he is bound to respond to his adverse environment differently than does someone without such feelings. If he is indignant and displeased with his fellow students, naturally he will respond to them with irritation and annoyance. He finds the adverse conditions an easy excuse to justify his ill feeling toward them.

The student who is interested in other people can understand their needs, and it becomes easier for him to tolerate a reasonable amount of their annoyances. It is when he is anxious over some current pressure and concern with himself that he is sensitive to distractions from his environment. The anxious and self-preoccupied person is easily interrupted by annoying stimuli. It is the student's attitude toward annoyances that creates tension in him which interferes with his concentration and with his motivation to do his work.

By the same token, some students cannot study or write an exam when someone is watching them nearby; they become anxious when they notice that they are being observed, due to the fear that something undesirable about them, of which they are unaware, will be exposed. This phenomenon is not uncommon and it is mainly related to sensitivity associated with their interpersonal conduct, e.g., self-consciousness, or a feeling of being criticized by someone. Although they may not always be fully aware of these explanations, the ultimate reasons inevitably are deep-seated inferiority feelings which the students have not been able to recognize and overcome.

Another reason for his inability to study and concentrate is that he is too absorbed in himself, or in areas of life which are more important to him than his academic duties. On the other hand, many students devote nearly all of their time to studies alone, and feel left out from extra-curricular areas which can offer them deep and gratifying experiences. If these "void" areas are satisfied, it will be easier for them to find more contentment in their studies as long as they do not devote excessive time to them. The student's whole personality has diversified interests which need to be expressed and cultivated.

The best way for the student to derive satisfaction from his work is to divide his time in varied activities. Surely, the student, like any gainfully employed person, must, at times, perform tasks in which he has little interest. These tasks can become more pleasant to him if his work is diversified, if he does many other things that are satisfying to him, even if they do not necessarily prepare him for a profession. Such activities are not necessarily a "waste of time" unless they monopolize the student's time at the expense of his academic load.

Some students experience a total lack of interest in any activity; nothing seems to arouse their interest. Most of these students have not even tried activities on a trial and error basis to see if something else will interest them. One cannot think out what should be the best thing for him to do, unless he has some experience with various types of work and recreation. The real reasons for his apparent lack of interest stem from a deep fear of involvement, a need to escape any unpleasant reactions from others or to avoid facing his felt weaknesses which could become more visible if he allowed himself to express his needs or to challenge his abilities.

### The Concern for Achieving Academic Success

Experience has shown that intelligence alone is not sufficient for high grades and post-college success. Personality attributes such as eagerness to learn, determination and enthusiasm may be more decisive factors than mere intelligence. The student's state of mind is the force that determines whether he will use his intellectual ability. Intelligence is imbedded in the personality, and, in most cases, the latter has to be modified if the student's academic performance is not consistent with his real ability, for negativism, depression, conflicts with people, and many other psychological factors are frequently responsible. Many of these problems can be rectified with counseling or brief psychotherapy.

Grades are important factors for the college student because they reasonably indicate his academic achievement. Although for some students, high grades mean maintenance of a scholarship, entrance into graduate school, etc., others desire to maintain very high grades because they derive satisfaction from having superior records. As long as the concern and worry over high grades does not cause the student emotional discomfort or distract him from studying effectively, this need is perfectly acceptable. It is not wise for him to concentrate solely on high grades at the expense of being left out of other social participations which are equally rewarding, for it is just as important to maintain a healthy and effective personality as it is to have high grades. High grades will usually be obtained when the student intends primarily to master and remember the material. High grades alone do not assure the student success in life. It is what he learns that is significant and not simply the numerical grade average that he maintains.

The concept of success is relative to the individual student. If, for example, a person with an I.Q. of 80 works in a bakery wrapping loaves of bread all day, he is considered to be successful; he is most likely performing up to his capacity. It would be difficult and completely unrealistic for him to attempt to comprehend principles of advanced trigonometry. On the other hand, a very bright student who is doing average work is not considered to be very successful when his above-average potential is considered. With counseling, such a student can learn better study skills or other techniques for improving his learning capacity. If he does not improve, then the real reasons for his lack of success may be of a psychological nature.

A common mistaken assumption among college students is automatically to equate a high degree of intelligence with good judgment and emotional maturity. Such a correlation is not always true; it is quite possible for a bright student to be lacking in common sense, as contrasted with an average student who can be relatively more stable and level-headed. In fact, many students compensate for their average intelligence by their ability to make realistic decisions, to be methodical and well-organized in their work, and to know beforehand precisely what is expected of them. The student who complains of not having ability in most cases is probably looking for an excuse; he may not have learned the techniques of study, or he may be in the wrong curriculum. Everyone has special abilities; however, the ability in itself does not mean very much without the proper motivation behind it. Why some students do not have motivation may depend upon a psychological reason.

Quite often, the student performs well in an area despite test results which did not indicate potential success in that area. The reason may lie in the fact that tests do not measure the student's motivation or his eagerness to do well. A student can succeed even with moderate ability, if his interest in a particular field is strong. In other words, tests tap only one aspect of one's personality; consequently, test results do not show the whole picture of the student's interests, aptitudes, and abilities. This is why the results should usually be interpreted by an expert in the field of testing—the vocational counselor. Identifying the student's talents and aptitudes is the chief concern of a large branch of applied psychology which is referred to as vocational counseling.

Since psychological tests are frequently used in colleges and universities for different reasons (vocational and educational choice, surveying study habits, underachievement, emotional problems), a few comments are in order to clarify in the student's mind the meaning of psychological tests and what they can actually do for him. Psychological tests commonly used in colleges are not infallible indices for predicting the student's future. They indicate to the student what he *can* do—not what he *should* do. They give the student clues regarding the areas where his potentials may be; it is eventually up to the student to decide what he wants to do. In order to make a decision, he may need some additional information to guide him in the proper direction. If tests are used with discretion and with good judgment, they can provide the student with a valuable source of information about himself.

A few words should be said about the meaning of the I.Q., since the term is so often used by students and educators. As with any other type of ability, intelligence is but one factor in the picture of the total personality. Although high intelligence is an important concomitant for success, other personal characteristics are just as important. Being persevering, methodical, and devoted to college work may be even more important than a high level of intelligence. Enthusiasm and alertness are often excellent visible characteristics of the successful student. If, by comparison, one student's I.Q. is lower than another's, it may mean simply that the first student must work a little harder than the second in order to obtain the same results. I.Q. scores are seldom given to students because they may misinterpret the significance of such a measure when it is given in numerical terms. Therefore, he may unnecessarily develop a false picture of his mental abilities.

A word can be said about the student's goals that are formed from his direct association with his fellow students and members of the faculty. Informal discussions on vocational goals can be very fruitful and enlightening to the student. Likewise, he can come into direct contact with members of a given profession, and by examining the various aspects of that particular vocation he can begin to sense how realistic are his own psychological make-up and emotional preparedness for that type of work. One cannot desire something without knowing what it is. Therefore, the greater his familiarity with the requirements and duties of a vocation, the more suitable his choice will be.

The student who is not performing up to his ability or who cannot achieve his desired goals is often handicapped by the fear that he will fail if he really tries. Such fears are formed chiefly through past experiences, when his attempts were met by rejection, disgrace, ridicule, discouraging comments, unworthiness, or criticism. These past experiences become associated with any subsequent attempts to succeed; hence, the resulting fear prevents him from trying to reach a goal consistent with his capabilities. He becomes so convinced of impending failure that he gives up any effort to rectify his attitude, analyze the situation, or to attack the problem systematically. A counselor can be of invaluable help in these situations. Often, the student's criterion of success is out of proportion with his self-image. Success is measured in terms of one's strengths and weaknesses. He is considered a success to the extent that he reaches his potential. The concept of success has a relative meaning according to the abilities of each individual, and not all students have the same potential.

Students evaluate their failures according to how they feel about themselves, and upon the degree of their self-confidence. For the student who has lost his courage to do college work, any minor mistake can mean that he is "stupid." He will be sensitive to anything that makes him appear *less*, as he compares himself with someone else. On the other hand, the student with high self-esteem and confidence is not frightened by the normally occurring periodic failures. When the student perceives himself as being inferior to others, his mind is geared to looking for clues in his environment which convince him that he is a failure. Psychologists have shown that the way a person reacts to the world around him depends considerably on how he feels about himself. For example, the student who says very little in class may be afraid that if he said anything the instructor will find his response unacceptable. The student acts *as if* people around him will not find his contributions worthwhile; thus, he shuns work and his academic performance deteriorates.

Sometimes a student can be so afraid of failure that he becomes almost totally handicapped. As with success, failure is not always as complete as the student assumes. Furthermore, the student should realize that not all people perform all tasks with the same degree of skill. Even very capable persons can fail a task in which they have no interest, or for which they lack sufficient aptitude and training. Yet, these persons cannot be called failures any more than can a successful business man who is unable to translate a passage of Homer. If the reasons for one's failure in college are real (illness, lack of talent, or interest), then there are ways by which the condition can be rectified. This process of investigation begins by discovering what the student can do, and then his interests are evaluated to see if he wants to do a particular type of work for which he has aptitude. By the evaluative process, a student can obtain assistance to formulate meaningful goals; and if he has varied interests and adequate aptitude for them, he can be guided to expand his depth of interest.

When the student is concerned with being always at the top of his class, he may be asking for more than he can handle if his ambition is not in line with his abilities. To compare himself with an ideal level of achievement may do him more harm in the long run than will his high intentions do him good. Actually, the ideal goal is seldom achieved. The student will save himself fruitless effort and discontentment if he develops his potential without reference to an external yardstick. He can still come close to being perfect if he cultivates and is able to make the best use of his talents. Every person does not have the same concept of an ideal for himself; rather, the ideal is meaningful insofar as the individual student is able to perfect himself within his own limits. The student should create his ideal out of his own objective assessment of himself, rather than out of a universal ideal, i.e., what all people should be.

Students often develop an erroneous attitude toward the threat of academic failure. At times, their reasoning out of the consequences that will follow failure is not logical. A lower grade in one course, or maintaining lower than average grades in a curriculum, causes the student to think that he is a "stupid" and worthless person, that he wastes his time and, consequently, ought not to be in school. Then, he proceeds to feel that no one will have respect for him, that his friends will discard him, that he will embarrass his parents, and that his whole future is completely ruined. A counselor or psychologist can help some students realize the error in their thinking, and can help them to find an area in which they can achieve success.

Another false conclusion students often arrive at is that no one is ever supposed to make mistakes. If this were true, everyone would be automatically disqualified from his present work. Mistakes are important mainly in the attitude the student holds toward them—what stand he takes on them. Mistakes can be reduced but not completely eradicated. Worrying over mistakes is not a helpful practice; it may even increase the incidence of mistakes. In many instances, mistakes result from other factors (compulsiveness, anxiety) in the student; hence, attempts to eradicate mistakes can be fruitless unless the effects from these factors are reduced. Finally, the student can worry less about his mistakes when he senses that others are unconcerned by these mistakes.

## Dependence and Autonomy from Parents

The student should realize that although he is making many decisions for himself, he is still dependent on his parents or other parent-like figures for many decisions which he is not quite capable of making for himself. He is financially dependent on his parents, even though the financial dependency will decrease considerably after he earns his degree. The student often is resentful when he feels that although he is acting independently of his parents, he still has the need to consult them, and even becomes "homesick" when he is away from home for a while. In other words, he needs his parents but he does not want to admit this need to himself. The student must face the fact that part of his normal growing up process includes a period when he is neither fully independent nor totally dependent upon his parents and adults in general. He should also recognize that during this period his feelings toward his parents can vacillate between love and hate.

Attending college tends to prolong the student's dependency and to stress the development of the mind more than that of the body. The student becomes intellectually productive, but his sexual production and marriage are delayed. He has to ignore, or give little importance to satisfying basic drives, while intellectual cultivation is stressed. The result is that he may still feel that he is a "boy" and that he is incomplete and subordinate to his parents. These feelings can interfere with his studies and his social relationships. Furthermore, while the student is striving for his independence, he may be afraid to lose the closeness that he maintains with his parents—especially if they are subsidizing his education. Most students outgrow their dependence, but some may deliberately neglect their studies and become critical of education or hold contempt toward students who earn better grades, in order thus to achieve their independence and manhood. This method is deceptive, for it gives the student only a temporary triumph. The student who wants to be emancipated from his parents and achieve his independence in his own right can do so by attaining his degree.

Occasionally, what the student learns in college can become a challenge to his parents who expect him to remain the same as he was in high school. There is always some kind of change taking place in everyone simply as a result of maturity but this change can further be guided by the amount of education one receives from college. The fact is that some students either harbor inadequate and erroneous values, or simply do not have any values at all and are searching for new ones. When the student feels he is being understood by those he esteems, he more easily puts order in his life so that he can fulfill his own interests and aspirations, and at the same time he recognizes and respects those of his parents.

The college student does not achieve his independence overnight, but he goes through a period of vacillation between the extremes of dependency and independence. This conflict is typically shown, for example, when the student asks his professors and parents for advice, and then becomes angry at them and at himself for "needing" them. In other words, he desires to be guided, but when assistance is forthcoming he rejects it. Such inconsistency is very typical of the dependence-independence conflict. The clash diminishes in favor of greater independence as the student feels he is accomplishing something as a result of his own decision and initiative. Fortunately, most students outgrow this struggle because the college atmosphere, although exacting control and conformity in many areas of life, also encourages and expects the student to develop skills whereby he learns to think and work independently.

Some parents do not know what to do, or do not understand this period of stress for the student; instead of gradually allowing him more "rope" while letting him *know* that he has been given more freedom, they tend to curtail his quest for independence. As the student's relationship with his parents worsens, he finds good reasons to rebel against them. Most students desire to establish their independence without really breaking the ties with their parents. If for every move he makes to become independent he is made to feel guilty by his parents, he will invariably have difficulty attaining his desired independence. On the other hand, if he is searching for independence just to spite his parents, he will inevitably meet with further problems. But if the student is convinced that, in order to attain sound mental health, he must feel *capable* of creating his independence *gradually*, without feeling forced to do so, then he will have less difficulty reaching his independence.

Unfortunately, our society tends to push students to do things in some areas, for which they are not prepared, and to impede their emotional growth in other areas. For example, the student's parents may be treating him like a child by forcing him to attend college, but may leave his course of study entirely up to him. The student can sense inconsistency in these parents which can intensify whatever minor resentments he may already have toward them. The student may use his need for independence as a rebellious gesture against his inconsistent parents. In fact, the student often normally vacillates between extreme dependency on or independency from parents, until he eventually reaches an ideal middle point.

The dependency-independence conflict operates throughout the entire life span of every person, but during the years of late adolescence and early adulthood it becomes most pronounced. Independence requires increased responsibility, which is not always accepted with enthusiasm by the college student. It can cause frustrations and tensions especially in the student who is not prepared to accept it. In other words, independence can be a painful experience, and some students who are not willing to assume the new status of increased self-reliance can sense independence as a threatening experience which they may want to avoid. Yet, everyone wants to be unrestrained and free from emotional and economic ties. In fact, the quest for independence is a desirable sign of maturity. It is the manner in which he seeks it that can spell the difference between adjustment and maladjustment.

Autonomy does not mean that the student should separate himself from his parents. It means that, while he still has certain obligations toward them, he is becoming more capable of living as an independent individual, and of making decisions for himself. As he becomes equal to his parents he is still emotionally close to them, although he has become more independent when compared with former years. To become negativistic and contemptuous toward parents is not considered as a move towards autonomy, but more as a reaction of hostility for personal reasons. The ideal situation is for the student to continue his associations with parents, and at the same time achieve his independence.

The threat of impending separation from parents may create anxiety in the student. This is a normal phenomenon that takes place between people whose emotional ties have been close. It is referred to as *separation anxiety,* and it subsides with time. For the emotionally healthy college student, separation from parents means a new challenge to him, whereby he is given the opportunity to master a novel situation. Separation should be accepted pleasantly, since it implies a stepping stone toward adulthood. Sometimes, separation may become difficult for the student and cause him to feel guilty if he thinks that by attaining autonomy he is leaving out his parents. If his parents have doubts about him, it becomes his responsibility to assure them that he can handle problems by himself.

Since every college student has already been through childhood and early adolescence, it can reasonably be assumed that he has been dependent on his parents, in varying degrees, for emotional and financial support. Simultaneously, he had to learn to harmonize his needs with the demands of society, give up some of his autonomy, and curtail his impulses. Consequently, he is bound to feel some resentment toward the parents. As the student reaches toward adulthood and independence, these resentments diminish. If the process of maturation is impeded, the ill feelings toward the parents can be strong enough to breed guilt, which easily precipitates other undesirable symptoms such as depression or anxiety.

Quite often, a student seeks help because his own interests are in conflict with those of his parents. For some, this may be a difficult situation because parents do not seem to understand the student's special problems. First of all, the student should realize that parents *do* have an obligation to advise their offspring of those things that are for his best advantage. Secondly, the student owes it to his parents to understand *their* needs. The student can discuss the matter with his parents in an objective way and reach an agreement that will be for the benefit of all concerned. However, this is much more easily said than done. Often after such a discussion, the problem can become more complicated, can result in more tension and hostility between the student and his parents, and can raise more problems than were initially present.

The student who has difficulty communicating with his parents should consider *their* upbringing; he should tolerate their shortcomings, and expect them to make mistakes, especially if they have little education. The student gains nothing by not respecting his parents. Everyone is aware of the "battle of generations." But the student himself is just as responsible for getting along with them, as they are with him. Since he is still dependent upon them, he can learn to compromise instead of fighting them. He should understand and recognize that his parents may be threatened by his greater knowledge and increased status, if they happen to be less educated, or they may be disappointed because he chose a field inferior to their expectations and ambitions.

The student can realize, furthermore, that his parents are not expected to be perfect in raising children, and that they often try to give or create in their children what they themselves wanted and missed in life. This attitude in parents may result in excessive and unnecessary discipline. Another tendency of the parents is to encourage the student to follow a career either typical of the family tradition or directly away from it. Finally, when the parents are maladjusted toward each other and the student is affected by it, he can seek professional advice to learn how he can cope with them. In all such cases, the student should above all, understand that if all adults are to be respected, then his own parents should be even more so.

Many students who enter the university soon begin to realize that their desire to pursue higher education was a need to please their parents' notion of success and achievement. Parents who feel somewhat unsuccessful in their lives have a tendency to persuade their offspring to achieve what they themselves were unable to attain. In order to achieve their ends, parents may attempt either to bribe their children by monetary indulgence in order to alleviate the guilt over their failure in life, or attempt to control their offspring by sacrificing their own well-being to make the children feel guilty.

Students that have been indulged by parents adopt submissive attitudes in social situations, and try excessively to please others in order to feel accepted by them. Others become psychologically infantile and become helpless in situations where they have to make independent decisions. In general, they become socially withdrawn individuals. Those who feel rejected by their parents have a tendency to appear shy and timid, and might even feel that everyone is rejecting them. Others adopt a hostile and revengeful attitude to everyone, and seem to be rejecting others the same way they were rejected.

The student wants to feel that whatever he does is the result of his own decision. The moment he feels that his parents are planning everything out for him, he feels that he is losing his individuality and self-esteem. He begins to sense a lack of worth as an individual, and feel that he is being used to gratify the needs of his parents. It is often observed that the student develops mental and physical symptoms (tiredness, sleepiness, laziness) when it becomes apparent to him that he is being treated as a robot, as a "thing" so to speak. Such a student can learn to compromise, to understand the needs of his parents, and to gradually achieve his independence from them. It is better to face the problem with his parents than to "get even" with them by employing a passive-destructive attitude, such as failing in college. Nothing is really accomplished by alienating himself from his parents. The student wants to feel that his parents are neither oversolicitous nor disinterested, but supportive and encouraging. He can achieve this condition by having a frank talk with them. If such an attempt is unsuccessful, the parents can be seen by a member of the mental health team in college; with this type of cooperation very effective results can be achieved.

Independence from parents requires a reasonable amount of conformity to society's rules. The world would become chaotic if people did not agree on certain rules about what their conduct should be. It would be difficult for any society to survive if its members did not believe in a common code of living, or did not agree on what is right and wrong. It is essential that the student know what his particular society condones and rejects, since these established codes have considerable usefulness in the survival and growth both of himself and of his society; they reflect the wisdom of many ages. In fact, contrary to some students' beliefs, regulations are not simply coercive techniques to make one confrom, but mostly they guarantee his freedom and individuality; freedom, however, does not mean that one can break regulations for his own needs. The student, then, can recognize that observance of the rules of society and college guarantees harmony in the functioning of its individual members, and take into account the long range needs for survival.

The pressure of having to conform can be a dreadful and baffling experience for the beginner in college. Conformity exists essentially everywhere in our society, and the student is apt to find it in college. The sensible student will realize that through cooperation he will make himself accepted, he will develop an identity, and his activities will be channeled to give him clear perspectives of the future. It is not so much that the student is molded into the desired pattern of how a college student ought to be and act, but that he is provided with the emotional and intellectual stimuli that enhance his growth toward maturity—a growth which implies control of hostility and resentment, and reasonable compliance with the established norms. He can still change these norms, if he wishes, in a critical and constructive way. A typical example of conformity is the fact that everyone is expected to wear clothes. However, every person dresses according to his own taste and budget.

## The Problems of the Commuting Student

The current trend of establishing community or urban junior colleges has increased the number of commuting students. In contrast to the large universities, these colleges often do not have a distinct social culture of their own, since they usually serve as a stepping stone in preparing the student to further his education elsewhere. With some exceptions, commuting students engage mostly in off-campus activities, and their attachments and identity with the junior college is not particularly strong. In such colleges, the student body is apt to be of diverse socio-economic backgrounds. The students tend to participate in relatively weak social relationships and group memberships at a local college, because they do not live in the institution, and hence do not spend much time with each other.

Some students mentally and emotionally bloom a few years later than their peers, and in such cases, living at home and commuting to college is justifiable. The potential college candidate should not feel that he should go away to college in order to "grow up and mature," simply because it appears the proper thing to do. One or more years commuting to a local college may help him improve his study skills and formulate goals, so that, when he moves to the college campus, he is prepared to pursue his objectives with fewer difficulties and more confidence. The transition to college should be gradual for such students.

On the other hand, a reasonably mature and emotionally independent student may go away to college immediately after completing high school without experiencing significant emotional consequences. Such students have done well in high school and, barring unforeseen circumstances, have formulated a fairly stable goal for themselves in college. It is sometimes difficult to determine who is really capable of living away from home. The matter becomes more complicated for the student when his parents urge him to attend a residential college because his studying away enhances their prestige in the eyes of the community.

The transition from a local junior college to a university or college away from home may become an easier task for the student than if he attended a residential college right after high school. He is apt to be better oriented and better able to find himself in the social and academic environment away from home. Although some educators feel that staying at home may actually prolong the student's dependency on his parents and stifle his emotional growth, one or two years at home should not make a great difference where his emotional growth is concerned, since he has an opportunity to become better adjusted to the academic demands of the junior college. However, should the home environment be severely stressful (alcoholic parents, delinquent siblings, undesirable neighborhood), the student will obviously prefer a residential college.

Living at home can be less advantageous for the student because of the distance in commuting to college, fewer opportunities to make friends among his peers, a home situation which is not conducive to studying, the annoyance of siblings and of unexpected guests, and constant unnecessary demands and supervision by parents. They may be too involved with their own problems, or fail to understand the student's needs; they may expect him to do excessive house chores, or interfere with his desire for privacy. Living on campus, on the other hand, can provide more independence for the student, a more relaxed environment, proper study conditions, more athletic and extra-mural activities, greater opportunity for meeting suitable peers of the opposite sex, and a general feeling of independence.

The above factors, however, can also be reversed. The student on campus, for example, may feel lonely, unable to do his work or to find a suitable place to study, he may lack dates and companionship with peers and feel isolated. The commuting student, on the other hand, may feel relatively independent at home, he may have understanding parents, an enjoyable circle of friends and excellent study conditions. The student should not arbitrarily value one situation over the other, but first estimate the conditions at home and college, and choose the one which best suits his own needs. In the final analysis, the student's personality characteristics, personal values and maturity, and ability to adapt, whether on campus or at home, are most important. Whatever his choice, the criterion of preference should be based on how conducive it is to his personal and emotional growth.

While a great number of students commute for entirely realistic financial reasons, a few who have the financial means and intellectual capacity to take advantage of a residential school choose to live with parents and commute. Such students tend to be isolated from their peers, do not date, cannot express themselves easily, and are emotionally very close to their parents. They feel more secure at home, and their felt social inadequacies may make them appear awkward in a residential college. Prolonged close living with parents can create resentment, especially if the parents have a lower socio-economic and educational background. They may feel antagonized by the student whose increase in education poses a threat to them. At times, parents may wish the student to live at home because of their own feelings of insecurity.

These students should realize that eventually they will be expected to achieve a sense of independence and responsibility and to identify themselves outside their own families with meaningful groups, professions, and persons important to them; that growing up means that one is expected to live independently and create his own identity and goals, without feeling guilty or having to antagonize or alienate his parents in the process. These identities and goals can be more easily attained at a residential college where the student's ties with his family gradually weaken. Many large universities offer facilities and expert personnel to assist the student with problems which he or his parents have not been able to solve.

### Relating with Peers

The student who first arrives on the campus comes into contact with both a new academic and a new social experience. Very frequently, one of these factors is influential upon the other. The student is open to new friendships which he tends to rely upon and confide in whenever personal difficulties arise. It would be most natural for him to turn first to his roommates, fellow-students, or to dating partners for solutions and suggestions for his immediate problems. Undoubtedly, many students do find solace and encouragement from those who seem to have had more experience and are able to make use of their reasonable suggestions.

Although individualism is stressed in our culture and in the academic environment, students are not completely independent of one another. There is exchange of ideas that leads to new insights, and to personal growth and maturity. Each student has unique experiences which can have a beneficial influence upon the others. But we must not forget that the confused ones add to the adolescent turmoil. The wise student selects those experiences from others that are conducive to his welfare and to the benefit of society, while he rejects those that are not. This process requires a sense of critical discrimination and a reasonable amount of maturity.

One of the tasks of education is to create adaptable personalities—capable of making the proper discriminations in social and academic situations. That is, the student learns to differentiate one fact from another without using mistaken assumptions. For example, a professor famous in his field may not necessarily be an interesting lecturer; in other words, knowing a subject and teaching it are two different talents. One cannot assume that an expert in a specific field is equally capable of communicating his ideas to others. Another common error is the failure to distinguish fully the biases and misconceptions that are held by the different social groups in college. The power to make discriminations in an objective manner is acquired through experience and is one of the important characteristics of the mature personality.

Every stage of human development is confronted with characteristic stress conditions which the individual must resolve. Many problems arise as the natural outcome of the transition from childhood to adulthood. Most typical seems to be the experience that many students feel, namely, that they are in college to excel, but have not been prepared emotionally to meet the host of other demands in college life which are by-products of academic stress. The student finds it very easy to isolate himself socially for the sake of academic success, until the time comes when he realizes that he has been left out of things and has missed the pleasant experiences that college life has to offer. At times, the opposite can be true, i.e., the student feels pressure from peers to behave according to their standards. He sometimes fears rejection if he does not go along. Actually, the student should decide for himself between what he desires and what he should do.

Every student who desires to grow emotionally and intellectually develops in the desired direction by cultivating friendships. Many students who are beginning their college careers tend to be "clinging vines" on other students in order to derive support and to gratify their dependency. When such students look upon their friends as providers, they soon lose them and any friendship that existed will disintegrate. Making excessive demands upon others and constantly complaining about everything are not conducive to friendship. On the other hand, students who feel too confident about their physical attractiveness may be prone to manipulate others and to use them to their advantage. Neither type of interaction, of course, is true friendship.

Nor is the number of friends and having a socially outgoing personality an index of emotional health; rather, what is important is the quality, duration and intensity of human relationships. There is a great difference between the student who has a few close friends in whom he can confide, and the student who has many distant, superficial and merely "visible" friends. These social attitudes can be an outgrowth or a cause of personal maladjustment. The student should accept the fact that he has emotions and feelings which can become expressed as he socializes with his peers, as long as these do not impose upon them. If he is afraid to make social thrusts, it may be from a fear that his need for acceptance and recognition will not be satisfied, or that he will uncover undesirable aspects of his personality which he does not want to face and admit to himself.

The excessive expression of, or the lack of, emotional spontaneity has become a problem for many a student. By nature, man has feeling and emotions on the one side, and thinking and reasoning capacity on the other. The aim of education is to promote both emotional and intellectual growth. It is healthy for the student to express emotions, as long as he is not overwhelmed by them. Sadness and enthusiasm, for example, elicited by a sports event or a play are healthy expressions as long as they do not become of long duration, and of strong intensity, and occur at an appropriate time. The student who easily becomes emotional and dramatic over relatively minor things in order to get attention is only looking for secondary gains; his emotions are no longer a means for healthy self-expression.

On the other hand, there is the student who is perplexed and bewildered, cannot decide what courses to take, where to go for recreation, or what to do in his spare time. Obviously, this student was not prepared from his early life to take responsibility and to make decisions for himself. He can be strongly convinced that he is incapable of academic work, and that no one really cares for him. In such cases, parents may have played an important role in forming these attitudes in the student that make him feel rejected and unwanted.

Feelings of rejection, in the college student, can be associated with relatively minor incidents (e.g., avoidance by a friend) which actually should not cause any mental distress or emotional turmoil in him. What probably happens, in most cases, is that he places a high premium on continuously maintaining perfect relationships with other people. Although this feeling is satisfying, it is too idealistic; other people have their prejudices, etc., which can cause them to act as they do.

When the student feels he has been rejected, he should realize that it may have very little to do with his own intrinsic value as a person. The student can look upon the situation from this point of view: Does he make some sort of selection when he chooses his friends? He obviously prefers some persons more than others. Does this mean that those he prefers the least should feel rejected? In the same way, one who desires to purchase an automobile does not usually drive away with the first one he sees on display. When one person seeks out another person, the benefit has to be mutual if their association is to be sustained. For this reason, some persons will be accepted while others are rejected, as a consequence of choice which is mutually satisfying.

What the student can do when he has been rejected by people is to search for new experiences that will bring him satisfaction and make him feel accepted and recognized for his worth as a person. But many students tend to give up easily after their first experience with rejection, and to feel sorry for themselves. This attitude is obviously unhealthy if it is strong and prolonged. If the student had experienced many rejections earlier in life, he would tend to feel more insecure and inadequate when faced with subsequent rejections. On the other hand, some students with a history of rejections are better able to withstand current rejections because they seem to acquire a kind of "immunity" from the past experiences.

Occasionally, a student will say to himself: "What have I done to be treated this way? I have been a good person all of my life and I have never done anything to harm anyone. Do I deserve to be rejected? Is there something wrong with me of which I am not fully aware?" First, it may be that he was never really rejected in the first place, and that he too easily feels slighted when people are merely indifferent toward him. In other words, when others are not as friendly toward him as he wishes them to be, he takes this as a sign of rejection. Second, others may have real reasons to omit him from their company, just as he may have when he chooses *his* friends. Third, any normal and well-adjusted person must encounter some rejection, even if he is the best person in this world; history cites many great men who made enormous contributions to humanity yet were ostracized by those they helped.

### Dating and the Sex Drive

Dating, because it requires a fair amount of closeness to other people, may also arouse the student's emotions and impulses, and cause him to act in a way that violates his ethical standards. The student often solves this conflict by remaining socially inhibited, especially if he was emotionally involved once in the past and was punished or hurt, or if he had strict and controlling parents.

The student who is afraid to be himself and to express his feelings naturally may feel that the situation will get out of hand, and that he will not be able to maintain his equilibrium. This student could learn to express a moderate minimum of feelings without fearing any impending danger.

More common, however, is the association of emotions with sexuality. When two students of the opposite sex become close to each other, there is obviously an opportunity for sexual expression. They may become angry or anxious when they feel they may lose control of their impulses. When the student does anything of a sexual nature which is against his moral upbringing, he may develop guilt feelings or become angry at himself for allowing his impulses to get out of control and violating his ethical standards. When these feelings are present, the student may be unable to do his school work, and may develop other unpleasant symptoms which, in turn, can prevent him from showing any emotion at all. Irritability, avoidance of others, restlessness, depression and feelings of guilt can hinder him from normal human interrelationships. This type of student is usually unable to carry his academic load, and he eventually seeks help because his grades are falling or he cannot concentrate. He may sense no connection between his emotions and the violation of his ethical standards with academic failure.

The emotional problems of students can be reflected by the degree of their sexual adjustment. Promiscuity is not as prevalent in college as some people believe. The majority of college students usually conform to the accepted basic moral and sexual standards of our society, because they are informed on sexual matters and are willing to make use of their values; they recognize that it is worthwhile to postpone the gratification of their sexual needs. They seem to realize that higher education would normally require delay in their sexual outlets until marriage after graduation. As the student learns to compromise his sexual drive for the sake of obtaining his education while he is still young, he should not feel frustration and resentment.

It is usually the student who has a need to rebel, by questioning the accepted universal and traditional values, who would be prone to sexual permissiveness. Rebellion of this type in the male can be due to disrespect of females, to frustration in some other area, to a need to punish the parents, to "test" himself because of self-doubts about his own masculinity, to establish an image of the male that he would like to be, and a host of other reasons. Many want to gain popularity, to become accepted because they feel lonely and unfit in their social group. Still others feel frustrated for not having values and standards of their own, or become sexually permissive because they are immature and naive in their heterosexual relationships. Lack of identity may also make the student vulnerable to sexual permissiveness. Sexual permissiveness is not justified on the basis of showing cynicism toward the seemingly inconsistent standards of parents and teachers, or to the large size and anonymity of the academic institution.

The female student should realize that the male is more easily stimulated by and places more importance on sex, whereas the female is, generally, more interested in securing mutual understanding and a deep emotional closeness with the male. The male responds to sexual stimuli quickly, whereas the female is slower in sexual responsiveness; hence, she is in a better position to exercise control by recognizing the reality of this difference. It is not wise for the female student to appear seductive in her clothing and her manners. By acting seductively, she incites and provokes the male (sometimes being unaware of it), only to refuse his advances and frustrate him. The result is that she cannot maintain normal social relationships. In fact, she may become sexually intimate and realize later that it was due to her own seductive behavior.

Students can learn to manage their sexual emotions. There is a great variety of individual differences, and not all students experience the same intensity. Although proximity between members of the opposite sex does elicit emotional response, students can learn to terminate certain emotions as soon as they begin to experience them. Sexual stimuli, such as a romantic atmosphere or the touching of skin, will trigger the sexual emotions which function automatically. They do not subside easily even when the stimulus is removed abruptly. Hence, one must learn to relate with the opposite sex by not allowing the sexual emotions to come into play. Feelings of belongingness, devotion, sharing, mental closeness, security, and a sense of value toward someone of the opposite sex are much more enduring and are healthier modes of emotional expressions than are the various modes of sexual experiences.

Dating provides great opportunity for sexual experimentation. The student of either sex is entirely responsible for his behavior during dates; but, unfortunately, a few male students are not fully aware of their responsibilities and seek momentary pleasures, without considering the welfare and the consequences that sexual permissiveness will have on their partner. Despite the emphasis on equality among the sexes, the male is still considered the aggressive party and initiator in our society. But difficulties can ensue when the male student, after treating his female partner with consideration, expects her to "put out" at the end of the evening, as if it were a reward which he has earned for entertaining his date. This is simply an act of selfishness—not love. In fact, if genuine affection does exist, he would not have the need to make such self-centered demands on his date. The student should remember that *the real purpose of dating is for social and not for sexual reasons.*

Boredom and loneliness are not relieved by sexual intimacy, but through participation in nonsexual activities which do not arouse the sexual impulses. The college environment provides many such situations which do not cause sexual stimulation. Social, aesthetic, intellectual, athletic, religious, and vocational pursuits are typical activities which the student may find interesting and rewarding. It is up to the student to find out for himself which of these activities is best suited for him. The point is that if the student is happy with himself in these other areas, his need for sexual expression will diminish and he will be better equipped to deal with sexual abstinence during his college years.

To many students who attend a large university the problems pertaining to the social behavior and purpose of dating may become quite severe. The primary objective of dating is to relate to different members of the opposite sex on a social basis and to understand better one's own personality. A person develops emotionally and intellectually as he relates with others and acquires a feeling of personal identity and a sense of being accepted. He appraises himself as a person having certain values and abilities, and compares them with those of his social group. Other social experiences of dating include the pleasure of one's company, the acquisition of proper etiquette, the sharing of mutual interests and participation in social functions. Often, however, there is a tendency for many students to become emotionally attached to each other and they cannot separate themselves without feeling hurt and rejected.

Dating provides an excellent opportunity for students to widen their social contacts with members of the opposite sex. Such an attitude will certainly broaden their experiences, enable them to understand themselves better, and help them later in making a mature choice of a mate. Most students achieve a satisfactory relationship with a few members of the opposite sex without obligation or feelings of being personally committed to someone. Frequently, however, students have a tendency to "fall in love" after having a few dates, while their partners are not especially interested in becoming attached to anyone at this stage. Many persons easily become "clinging vines" and show a great dependency on the dates. However, such behavior often becomes a threat to their partners and causes them to withdraw.

Necking and petting may become a problem in dating. Many students feel guilty for having "gone too far," and frequently such activity results in loss of respect and in resentment towards each other, and may even precipitate a severe depression. When, during dating, two young people become physically close to each other, they may reach a point where against their better judgment they cannot control themselves. The consequences may be disastrous—especially for the girl who has to take the burden. She may feel shameful and worthless for not being able to live up to her moral standards.

Occasionally, there are some male students who desire to date in order to find out "how far she will go." In nearly all cases, they are rebuffed and then blame the girl for not being a "good sport." Those who are insecure about themselves like to "make out" to dispel any doubts they have about themselves. The student who feels relatively comfortable with himself and socially secure does not have the need to go out of his way to show he is a "real man." The same applies to female students. Social values on the campus advocate the "going steady" attitude as a means of enhancing one's prestige and acceptance by social acquaintances "because that's the right thing to do." Although the acquisition of status and conformity to social values lead into the need for "going steady," other factors may be involved such as using a date's social position to prove one's own ability for conquest or to impress one's peers.

Some students feel that premarital sex is acceptable as long as there is love and understanding between the partners. Others feel that going steady, being pinned, having agreed to become engaged in the future, or even being engaged gives the partners the right to become involved sexually. These attitudes can defeat the purpose of marriage and create conflicts later. Sexual permissiveness before marriage can breed infidelity, and contempt and mistrust for each other. It reduces the courtship to the physical level, and it may lead into pregnancy and forced marriage when they are not prepared for it yet. But the female suffers the most, for she is more prone to feel shameful and guilty when she decides if she should keep her experiences secret from the man she will eventually marry, or what will happen if he should find out. When the student accepts the idea that sexual intimacy was meant only for marriage, and that he will satisfy this legitimate need with the marital bond, he should be able to postpone this need until marriage, while tolerating occasional frustration normally associated with premarital abstinence.

The power that sustains the family, society, and the world is love. Maturity is achieved when the individual is capable of giving love without thinking of how much he receives. Every human being goes through stages in his emotional development— from receiving love without reciprocating, to giving love without asking for compensation. Hence, when a person is overly concerned that he be loved, he is too much preoccupied with himself and not enough with others. Such an attitude is self-defeating because the receiving of love depends upon how much one is capable of giving, upon how interested one is in the welfare of his fellow man. The truly mature person derives greater pleasure from giving love than from receiving it.

## Masturbation

A related problem of a sexual nature that students often worry about is the practice of *masturbation*. This practice should be considered as normal, in the sense that a very large number of students engage in it. Masturbation is very common and usual in college students, and it is not indicative of any pathology. It causes no known physical harm, and tends to diminish with age, and, naturally, after marriage. The practice tends to increase when the student is under tension, and it often serves as a means of releasing the tension. Masturbation is more common among those students who cannot establish satisfying social relationships, and who tend to be sensitive to others, shy, and introverted, for the simple reason that the practice is performed seclusively. Another very usual phenomenon among male students is the secretion of seminal fluid during sleep, with or without dreams. It is called *nocturnal emission,* and it is common and perfectly normal, especially in those students who do not masturbate very often.

The student should bear in mind that the possibility of going "insane," of losing his strength, and of being "weak" on account of his inability to control his practice of masturbation, may cause considerable distress to him, and an excessive preoccupation with the consequences. These inferences are entirely false and unfounded. His attitude toward masturbation has to change so that he becomes more relaxed over the practice and as his concern about it diminishes the frequency of masturbation will probably decrease. Excessive masturbation can have its roots in the student's need to remind himself of his masculinity and procreative powers. Also, those who feel extremely unhappy, depressed, and without love tend to practice masturbation in order to obtain pleasure. Obviously, excess is not ideal and should be avoided. The practice may diminish when the student can find social rewards that are far more pleasurable than the practice of masturbation.

## Sensitivity Toward Physical Characteristics

Physical defects, real, imaginary, or exaggerated, can generate unnecessary unhappiness and ill feelings in the student which may prevent him from making the best use of his intellectual and social abilities. He desires a pleasant physical appearance because it enhances his sociability with the opposite sex. It is more likely, because of the age difference, for the adolescent student to rely on his physical appearance for social success than for an older student. But as the student matures, he begins to find physical appearance less meaningful, and he is attracted by other qualities of a non-physical nature. Consequently, he pays less attention to his own physical features, as he outgrows his adolescence, and compensates by improving his personality.

The student's unacceptable physical characteristics are, for the most part, exaggerations of relatively minor features, and his reflections of his own insecurity are typical of his age. Actually, there is little relationship between physical appearance and success. If the student would notice adults and middle-aged people with physical characteristics similar to his own, he would readily admit they are loved, respected, accepted, worthy, and competent as any other person. Attitudes and feelings toward physical appearance stem from *within* the student rather than from the reactions of other people. The student who feels comfortable with the way he is can easily tolerate an occasional remark from another student.

People are not normally rejected or accepted because of their looks. It is mostly their psychological attitudes—cheerfulness, interest in others, toleration, tactfulness, sense of humor, and positive approach to life—which impress others. If the student sees a deficiency in his socialization, he should know that he can develop these traits. He can be held responsible if these qualities are absent, but he certainly is not responsible for his physical characteristics. Of course, the student will more readily blame his felt physical unattractiveness for his social underdevelopment, than to admit to himself his personality inadequacies.

Many college students feel embarrassed and even angry at themselves for having a physical condition which is not in harmony wtih their ideal image of themselves. Obesity, a tall or short stature, acne, disproportional limbs, small chest, facial features such as a light beard or a long nose—all may contribute to the way the student relates to other people. He reacts to others according to how he feels about himself. If he assumes that no one is going to tolerate his physical features, he may adopt a "don't care" attitude and become isolated and cynical. The co-ed who is self-conscious of a few pimples on her face can solve her dilemma by pretending to be too "busy" in order to discourage boys from becoming interested in her. Although self-defeating, this attitude is more acceptable to her than to make known to them that she desires dates but is never asked because they do not accept her physical appearance.

Another self-defeating attitude is the student's fear of criticism by those with whom he lives and works. Everyone has some physical characteristic which others like to laugh about; however, if he is sensitive over it and if he is not able to live with a personal idiosyncracy, he may eventually have a group of hostile people around him. The best way to deal with contemptuous comments and ridicule is for the student to *agree* with them! In this manner, he "takes the wind out of their sails" and simultaneously he does not lose his friends. People usually admire someone who can tolerate a reasonable amount of jocosity. If, however, it becomes too exaggerated, the student should begin to wonder more about the needs of these people than to treat himself as a real clinical case. One can easily understand how a student with strong feelings of inferiority and sensitivity over his physical features can become defensive and withdrawn, and cause great animosity in others toward himself.

## Normal Reactions to Temporary Stress

There is a typical phenomenon common among seniors which is described as the senior syndrome or "senioritis." It is considered normal and it very likely disappears quickly, soon after the student leaves college. These types of problems that the senior student experiences are primarily a reaction to a specific stressful situation which he has difficulty overcoming. As soon as the situation looks more promising, the student's feeling of distress diminishes. These problems do not imply any basic personality defect or maladjustment. Senioritis occurs because the student is faced with making many decisions at once which can have an important influence on his life. The problems he has to solve are relatively normal, and it is not so much their magnitude as it is the number of them that he has to cope with simultaneously. Incoming freshmen can feel the same experiences as they flounder through the first few weeks prior to finding themselves in college.

Specifically, the student may not only feel pressured when he enters college, but he may also feel the same strain when he is about to leave college. After a few years of college attendance, he is easily prone to become rooted and settled to the routine of college life. As he anticipates a new adjustment to another more or less unfamiliar situation outside college, he may begin to feel uncomfortable and uneasy over the anticipated change and greater opportunity for independence. Usually, the male student may not be too sure what he will do after graduation. He has a number of factors to consider: military service, marriage, a position in his academic specialization, the pursuit of a higher degree, anticipatory fear of adjustment to a new locale, a long trip, etc. These are the alternatives the student must choose from and the new conditions he must adapt to.

The female senior also tends to go through the same emotions and thoughts, but the reasons may be somewhat different. She is more apt to feel being in a "clutch" when her close friends and social acquaintances are about to disperse, each in their own way, with the pleasant anticipation of their forthcoming matrimony. She may feel that in college she had better chances of finding a prospective mate; that at the very end of her college career she is a failure if she is not dating steadily, pinned or engaged; and, that upon leaving college she will have to begin anew her mate selection, with ever decreasing possibilities. Female seniors may also have the problem of career choice as they consider such factors as salary, promotion, opportunity of meeting men, living with or away from family and friends, travel, etc.

In nearly all cases of female seniors who are matrimonially unsettled, these feelings are exaggerations; the fact that the other female seniors are well on their way to marriage does not logically follow that college is the *only* place where one finds a mate. Apparently, those who have not found a marital prospect in college are normally expected to feel uneasy about themselves, and even to question their personality, attractiveness, and personal worth as females, often wondering why they did not attract someone. Their concern for not having found a suitable mate in college may be quite legitimate. However, for many female students, the chances of meeting a more *eligible* and financially *independent* person are greater after she leaves college. This notion does not imply that those students who have chosen a mate wisely while in college are in any way considered as having erred.

In both instances, the problem of separation from college is not as severe as it may seem. The student is obviously uncomfortable, but the strain is apt to be aggravated by the emotional atmosphere of separation. Actually, these feelings are characteristic of this type of situation, and they usually diminish as soon as the student is removed from it. His "maladjustment" is superficial; it has a fleeting quality, and his response to these adverse situations is entirely normal. There is nothing wrong with the student's personality. The situation simply becomes overwhelming and difficult to handle. These problems are referred to as *situational reactions,* and they imply that the student is reacting to a transient type of stress situation. Below is a typical example of a normal reaction to stress.

A male, married, graduate student saw the college physician, complaining of insomnia, nervousness, nightmares, excessive worry, and inability to concentrate on his studies. He had been scheduled for his prelims a month hence, his wife was expecting a child in a few weeks, he was behind in his payments on his trailer, where he had been living with his wife and two children, and he did not have a position for employment after graduation. His funds had been exhausted, and he had not been able to secure another loan. These problems had been tormenting his mind, and he felt incapable of solving them one at a time without undue interference from the other problems. He had come to the point where he could not do anything; nor could he function well. Even fairly simple problems seemed insurmountable to him.

The student is a normal individual who developed symptoms on account of the pressure and the problems which he had to solve in a limited time. Therapy or any type of psychological treatment was not necessary, other than manipulating certain conditions in his environment. Actually what this student needed most were funds to meet his current and anticipated demands, and assurance that financial assistance will be forthcoming to him. The anxiety and worry over finances was strong enough to interfere with his studies. When an opening for a position and financial assistance were made available to him, his symptoms disappeared almost totally. After the first session, the student needed no further interviews.

## The Conflicts of Married Students

The social transition has changed immensely the status of women in our society. In the autocratic social structure she had very few choices to make, if any. Her role was to marry, become a homemaker and have children. In her family and her society, she had very little to say, and rarely ever had any considerable income or owned land. With the advent of the industrial revolution and World War I, her socioeconomic status began to change. Her emancipation took a more definite shape around World War II, and we currently witness her achievement in almost all professional fields which were formerly considered to be the exclusive domain of the male. Since her rights and privileges are equal to those of the male, she is allowed to compete with him in nearly every area. Although this change of status is humanistic and theoretically justified, it has brought a large number of conflicts and has made adjustment more difficult.

Many men today have difficulty accepting the notion that women are equal to them, and feel dethroned from the central position in the family that they formerly had. The woman, on the other hand, begins to feel guilty by deviating from her exclusively feminine role and becoming more aggressive. She is more confused about her social role and has not been able to cope with the sudden change in her status. Some women have realized that by repudiating their feminine role they alienated themselves from men, and as a result feel dejected, lonesome and anxious. Some men, on the other hand, feel demasculinized by women and attempt to strive harder for masculine identification and may end up by being unduly hostile and aggressive.

Traditionally, it is the male who pursues a career and is considered the breadwinner, whereas, the female is the house-keeper and raises children. With the advent of the democratic philosophy of equal rights, the female, besides her role as mother, wife, and housekeeper, wants a career. There is nothing essentially wrong for the female to desire a career in addition to marriage. But, once married, she may encounter conflicts if her career is *above* or even equal to marriage. As long as the married female decides that her marital duties and roles are more important to her than her career, there is little chance that she will have a *marriage vs. career* conflict. Also, a career breeds a competitive attitude in her, whereas marriage demands cooperation. If the married female student does not realize these basic attitudes, she may find difficulty with being married.

There have been a number of cases of married couples in college where the wife is postponing having children in the family, and she attends a few courses because she would like to "be back in school again." In other words, is her role to be a student, a wife and mother, or both? Some women become anxious or bored when they have to stay in the house many hours doing housework while their husbands attend college. Women are taught that they should "express and find" themselves, and that not to have a career is a handicap; thus, the wife of the college student who has to work to support her husband becomes easily frustrated when she feels deprived of a career. Experience has shown that these persons can alter some of their conflicting values which interfere with optimum adjustment in marriage. The female can realize that because she is married to a student, she will have to postpone some of her needs until after graduation.

Other problems of married students in college involve the husband's intellectual growth and status, when often the wife is left behind in these areas. By the time he graduates, he finds himself estranged from and disenchanted with her. Sometimes there is even lack of communication between them. Also, she may have to postpone having children because of work and lack of funds. The husband often tends to ignore his working spouse and appear less affectionate and demonstrative, and spends little time with her, because the attainment of his degree is more important to him during this period. The wife may feel some resentment because she has to give up her own education for the sake of her husband's. Tension also develops because of the strained relationship between them. Learning to accept and tolerate these conditions, allowing the wife to attend college on a part time basis, and making it a point to see each other more often are a few constructive approaches. However, for most students, these problems pass quickly, and diminish as soon as the husband's education is over.

Sometimes difficulties arise in married students when both attend college. In such a case, they need to accept both roles, student and spouse, without letting one interfere and conflict with the other. Such an arrangement can be difficult for some students. The situation may become more complicated when only one spouse holds a job, earns better grades, or is studying a field which is potentially more prestigeous and lucrative. The male is more apt to feel envy which he may be reluctant to express openly. Under these conditions, their children may pose a problem for them. It is difficult to furnish answers for solving these conditions, because each marital couple has unique qualities which must be considered. By tolerating the partner's needs, by discussing their aspirations as objectively as possible, and by showing devotion and patience, they can overcome most of these problems until graduation. Occasionally, married students, who attend college with very few difficulties, find themselves with problems after they complete their studies.

## The Dilemmas of Foreign Students

The increase of foreign students in American colleges and universities, particularly after World War II, has brought forth many new adjustment problems in campus life that are peculiar to the foreign student. In order to function on the American campus, he has to give up, at least partially, some of his values and adopt new ones with a minimum of guilt and anxiety. It happens frequently that his newly acquired attitudes have not been properly integrated into his personal system of values, but merely constitute a series of rituals to give the impression that he has really adapted to the new situation. Here he has to play an assumed role, in order to function and be accepted. Then, when a situation becomes demanding and threatening, he is more likely to lose control and uncover himself and experience a feeling of failure than is one who has made the real adjustment.

Problems with foreign students become more complicated when their maladjustment to American culture results in some hostility towards Americans which is not expressed for fear of more serious consequences. When the student reaches his homeland, he expresses his true feelings without fear of retaliation, and in some cases he may turn out to be a virtual enemy of the United States. Another factor that has a direct effect on foreign students is the rapid pace of American life and the demand that is imposed on them to maintain a certain amount of productivity if they want to be retained and succeed in their studies. Some foreign students fail in their studies because of personal conflicts and disturbances related to political or social unrest in their homeland.

Another typical problem is the foreign student's unpreparedness to accept some prejudice as a normal expression of fear and ignorance on the part of the American student. They often feel different from American students and, consequently, are apt to be sensitive even over the slightest and most harmless negative remarks that are made about them. Anxiety, arising from the above problems, from his concern over meeting academic standards in order to avoid deportation and rejection, from his long separation from his family, etc. can cause the foreign student to develop physical symptoms and to seek medical care from the college physician. But the real causes are often psychological. Unfortunately, foreign students are more prone to visit a medical doctor rather than to seek a counselor and discuss their feelings with him.

The differences of the new culture, being exposed to greater sexual stimulation and dating, differences in the food and social customs, the new methods of instruction, and the type of courses that are prescribed to them are but a few of the typical problem areas of foreign students. Also, difficulty with the English language is very common among foreign students. Some students become severely homesick, especially if they realize that they cannot return to their homeland until their studies have been completed. Many foreign students become anxious and perplexed when they realize that upon their return to their native land they will no longer enjoy as many privileges and facilities as they did during their stay in the United States. They may also feel that some of their native values are inferior to those that they found in the American university, and they may experience conflict when they attempt to instill American values in their homeland. Others, who have been aculturated to American values, may wish to remain in the United States because their country is either underdeveloped or politically unstable.

# 4

## SAFEGUARD DEVICES FOR ADJUSTMENT

Not all people are always capable of coping with the great variety of stress that exists around them. Most people exhibit a mild degree of tension or fear during uncomfortable conditions, when their self-esteem is being threatened, when they anticipate failure and rejection, and when they sense that their impulses, which are unacceptable to their own and society's moral code, will get out of hand. By nature, the individual's mind uses certain devices which are capable of protecting him from these feelings so that either he does not develop as much anxiety, or that he is able to control most of it. These stratagems are generally referred to as *safeguard mechanisms or mechanisms of adjustment*, because they assist the individual in maintaining his control and self-esteem, and they help him to adjust to stress. Said in another way, these mechanisms can establish an equilibrium between the person's own needs and the demands of his environment.

The ability to survive, to protect themselves from and adapt to a variety of stressful life conditions, is found in all living organisms. For example, animals develop thick layers of skin or special coloring in order to protect themselves against other animals, and to resist harsh weather conditions. The same principle applies to the mental and emotional life of man. The mind has the capacity to invent means by which it can avoid, neutralize, or forget whatever becomes disturbing, intolerable, and unpleasant to it. These means help to relieve tension and anxiety, and they give the person his desired recognition, sense of security, and feeling of self-esteem.

These safeguards are necessary and normal if one wants to live more comfortably. They shield the individual from the harsh reality of his inferiorities and inadequacies, so that he will not feel threatened or hurt. Some of these devices work automatically, while others are used deliberately. They are nature's way of helping the person to avoid the unpleasant aspects of his behavior. For, if he were to see himself exactly as he is, he may become concerned and deeply pessimistic over himself. On the other hand, if these mechanisms become too intensified and rigid, they become distracting and he has great difficulty functioning adequately in his environment. Although every student uses these safeguard mechanisms, he is not always aware of them. After reading about them he will become familiar with some, and he may be able to recognize certain ones in other students, and be more tolerable toward them.

The student solves his daily problems, and he achieves his goals in college through encouragement, motivation, and his social and intellectual skills. If he cannot cope with the difficulties by these means, the other alternative would be for him to shun society's expectations of him and to disregard the real issues of his life with which he is confronted in order to avoid facing his own inabilities. In order to escape from the dread of the awareness of his inferiorities, he may begin to act in a manner that prevents him from looking at himself realistically. This process usually takes place without the student's conscious efforts or awareness. Hence, prolonged and deep-seated conflicts cannot be effectively eradicated merely by reading about them, because they are usually accompanied by strong safeguard mechanisms which serve to minimize the stress that his conflicts may produce; the result is that the student cannot assess himself accurately, and he is bound to overlook the causes and effects in his behavior.

Every personality must have a reasonable degree and an adequate number of safeguard mechanisms in order to protect itself from its faults and limitations. The student can learn to *recognize* and *accept* these mechanisms in himself as long as he derives some relief from them; they should not cause him to divert his energy from his usual activities, or make him anxious and confused. An analogy can be seen in the amount of salt in the tissues of the human body. An excessive amount or a deficiency in salt may result in severe physiological disturbances. Yet, salt is considered to be one of the most necessary elements for life. The remaining portion of this chapter will be devoted to the typical safeguard mechanisms in college students, along with illustrated examples. *These examples are everyday occurrences in all normal students, and are not taken from case histories.*

## Compensation••

*When a person is attempting to develop a desirable trait in order to overcome an undesirable one, we say that he is compensating.* It is very admirable for the student to desire to make up for his deficiencies by excelling in an area in which he has interest and ability, as long as his choice of that particular field is also based on good judgment and realistic reasons; otherwise, instead of being able to overcome unacceptable traits, he may meet with more failure which is equally undesirable. Some students seem to make this mistake, not knowing that although compensation is a helpful mechanism, it may become totally undesirable when there is little judgment and objectivity involved. The aspiration described in the following student is an example.

> Mike wanted to enter the pre-med curriculum, but he only had average grades in high school and college. Despite these factors, he was accepted in the pre-med club. When his friends asked him what it was about medicine which attracted him, he replied that he had an older brother who had always done well in college, and who was currently an intern in medicine. Mike related further that he was also attracted to the idea that his brother wore a white coat with a stethoscope hanging from his neck, and was impressed when the nurses obeyed his orders and called him "Doctor." This type of compensation is fairly unrealistic because the motives behind it are not fully legitimate and adequate.

The physicially well-developed student who has difficulty qualifying for a professional career because of average ability may compensate for this lack by excelling in athletic pursuits for which he is qualified, and he becomes accepted because of his excellence in sports. By the same token, the physically un-attractive girl becomes proficient and prominent in a special field, so that she is admired and respected. Furthermore, some parents may want to cover up their own failures by setting up great expectations for their children. For example, an uneducated and financially unsuccessful father may want his son to acquire a college education, even though the son has little interest in college. The son may resent the father who forces him to attend college, and the father may become disturbed at his son's ungratefulness. If one compensates for his own demerits through someone else, he may create ill feelings and alienate the person involved.

Compensation is one of the best devices the student has to make up for his weaknesses and inferiorities, as long as the form of compensation he uses is socially desirable. Strong aggressiveness and unwarranted competitiveness are obviously not the best methods of compensation. Compensation does not imply that one should dominate and control others, and suppress their needs. But to overcome personal weaknesses, by achieving noticeable success through socially approved channels whereby society benefits from one's success, constitutes a constructive and useful mechanism. For example, one who lacks attractive physical appearance and is sensitive about it may join a gang and fight society in order to "prove" himself. However, he can also go through medical school and become a physician; in this way he makes up for his physical defects by becoming useful and needed in society.

The principle of compensation can be evidenced in more than one area of human behavior. There are three recognized types of compensation: *organic, social* and *psychological.* The mechanism of compensation is common in the human body. The function of organs which have become damaged and defective is often taken over by adjacent organs. If there are two organs present with the same function such as the adrenal glands, for example, and one becomes damaged, the other will compensate by hyper-trophying, and making up for the absence of the other's function. Similarly, when a portion of the liver is damaged by disease, healthy, undamaged portions will compensate by reproducing new tissue.

A similar organic compensation is the making up of physical debilities by excelling in the physical part of the body in which one is deficient. Many persons become famous dancers and skaters after having had polio in their childhood. More vivid is the example of Demosthenes of ancient Greece who overcame his stuttering to become a famous orator. In the social area, one may notice the male student dressed in unnecessarily expensive and immaculate clothes, or the girl wearing heavy make-up and with a conspicuous hairdo. Both may be attempting to divert others' attention from their own social shyness to their appearance. Presentable clothes can make them feel more comfortable in social situations. Finally, psychological compensation is shown in those who make up for their personal inferiorities by developing other admirable traits (thriftiness, industriousness). Another way is to devote themselves to activities in which they do not come into close contact with other people, so that they avoid exposing their personality, but still benefit mankind through their work, as with personal research, for example.

## Substitution

*Substitution is the mechanism by which the person, unable to reach a desired goal, relieves his frustration and anxiety by substituting for it a similar and comparable but more easily obtainable goal.* It involves the exchange of goals, the pursuing of one which is less difficult to obtain, but which still retains some characteristics of the original goal. Thus, when a goal cannot be avoided or overcome, it creates anxiety and distress in the person. If he tries to eliminate the goal, he may feel inadequate; if he tries to overcome it, he may actually fail. By pursuing a goal similar to the original one and more within the reach of his abilities, he lessens his anxiety and frustration. Below is a typical example of substitution.

Richard had been a very promising athlete in high school, but in college, with so much competition against him, he had not been able to succeed as he desired. He was always interested in sports, and he felt that his main talents were in athletics. He wanted to become a professional athlete, but after he realized this goal was unrealistic, he decided to pursue a degree in physical education for which he was better suited. Richard was unable to reach his original goal; neither could he leave the area of sports to which he was fully committed. By becoming an athletic coach he still remains in the field of his interest, but the condition is one in which his functions are compatible with his abilities. The transposed goal, although less glamorous, is similar to the original one, and he does not lose his self-esteem.

## Day-dreaming

*Day-dreaming as a safeguard device, constitutes a temporary mental retreat from the environment by means of which the student indulges in wishfulfilling type fantasy.* Day-dreaming usually occurs in those who cannot achieve satisfaction in their everyday activities which are seemingly dull to them, or who have not been able to gratify their needs through participation in real life activities. When the student feels discontent because he is not able to do the things he wishes, he easily achieves satisfaction as he finds himself day-dreaming. All normal students day-dream nearly every day, especially during the duller moments. It gives them a temporary relief from boredom, and it provides a few moments of relaxation during which they can regroup their energies and face their duties with greater strength.

Day-dreaming can vary between dreams of being powerful and performing great feats, as the Walter Mitty type fantasies, and thoughts of being humiliated and having suffered so that he can punish someone or make him feel sorry for him. In the first instance, the fantasies of male students becoming great scientists and heroes are very common, and of female students excelling in areas where physical beauty plays a significant role. In the second instance, he suffers in the day-dream in order to elicit revenge or pity, possibly from someone in real life who rejected him. In other words, the content of the daydream can have a meaningful purpose depending upon the needs of the student, his feelings toward people, and on how many of his aspirations he has not been able to materialize in real life. There are other types of fantasy besides these two just mentioned.

When day-dreaming becomes excessive in duration and intensity, it may become an undesirable mechanism, because prolonged withdrawal from the environment will ultimately defeat the student's achievement of his goals. Furthermore, he may become conditioned to day-dreaming and may find it difficult to shift his energies to people and the world around him. On the other hand, day-dreaming can be a satisfying experience when it occurs at the proper time of the day and in short intervals. For example, it is most beneficial to him when he day-dreams toward the end of the day after he has already prepared the next day's assignment. However, escaping into fantasy during times when concentration and initiative are required, in order to perform well in a certain task, is not helpful and should be discouraged.

It is quite possible for a chronic day-dreamer to be quite contented with himself and to cause no significant interpersonal disturbance. For example, the student who does poorly in college and barely passes his courses because he constantly day-dreams fictional achievements in order to satisfy his frustrations and underachievement in real life, may be quite happy with this kind of arrangement, but he is certainly far from being adequately adjusted. He remains socially invisible, and a non-participant and aloof toward life's responsibilities, and he does not develop himself into a fully integrated human being. In other words, a student can pose no problem to anyone and still maintain only a marginal adjustment to college life.

The content of daydreams changes with one's age. While children day-dream of possessing objects, adolescents and young adults have more heterosexually oriented, wishful fantasies. Day-dreams can be of help to the student's career, can assist him in overcoming the frustrations of studying, and can motivate him into actual success, as long as he also applies himself and expends actual effort toward achieving, in reality, the pleasant experiences of his wishful fantasies. It is satisfying to the student to dream of the rewards which his college work will bring him; in fact, it can make him into a more effective student. But if he day-dreams without applying effort or becoming involved in his work, he may not attain tangible success. Day-dreams reflect the student's current needs and the things he lacks in real life situations, as shown from the following example.

Ted is a handsome teenager who claims he never had a date. He feels very anxious in the presence of girls, and he has difficulty holding a simple conversation with them. He literally becomes panicky at the thought of even calling a girl. Ted likes to take long walks alone on Saturday night, and to imagine being with a luscious blonde who is very fond of him and admires him, although he has only a passive interest in her. He continues his fantasy by imagining another girl—a brunette, this time—who is equally in love with him. The girls now begin to argue as to who actually owns him. He enjoys watching them argue over him, and he displays a real grin as if he were actually witnessing this event. In reality, persons who happen to be strolling by notice his grin and wonder what he is thinking about. Finally, the conflict is resolved as he dreams of escorting both girls, one on each side. Ted is replenishing his lack of real feminine companionship through pleasurable wishful fantasies.

## Intellectualization

*By the device of intellectualization, the student detaches himself from situations which may make him act emotionally.* When emotionally provoking situations threaten to unleash his feelings, he attempts to view the situation with emotional detachment. An example of such behavior can be the policeman at the scene of an accident where quick judgment and objectivity is required. If he became hysterical over human tragedies, he would be unable to mobilize his skills and act responsively. By the same token, students who study literature containing emotional conflicts may unwittingly concentrate on the style of the author, the sentence construction, the idioms, etc., when asked to offer comments. Anything of an emotional nature becomes threatening to them. Naturally, this safeguard, like many others, is quite appropriate if not carried to an excess. Teachers and nurses are prone to be this way, and to be perceived by others as "cold" and undemonstrative.

The student can see that a moderate amount of intellectualization is a merit, since the control of emotions results in clear thinking and effective action when under duress. Excessive intellectualization, however, may result in role-playing; for example, the student does not express himself as he really feels but he rather hides behind abstract pursuits (music, art) and he finds the mundane activities of life disinteresting. He does not experience the emotional aspects of life (dating, parties) which are attractive to the well-balanced student. The result is that he exposes himself to only one side of life—the intellectual side—and he eventually feels the void created with this cleavage by a general feeling of emptiness, weariness, and depression. Following is the description of a student who intellectualizes excessively.

Ray complains that the practical aspects of his research project have been extremely frustrating and difficult to understand. All of his friends are described as being the "intellectual type," and he never has time for dates. He denies having any sexual needs or thoughts, and he belittles anything which is of a sexual nature. He feels that people in a situation may take advantage of him unless he is intellectually aware of the situation. Ray simply feels unable to cope with practical and concrete matters, but he is very capable of expressing himself verbally, and of describing situations in a most ideal and abstract way. He tries to avoid any difficulty with people by reclusion; therefore, he has no real friends, but instead, he derives immense gratification by constantly reading books. Ray controls his feelings and emotions excessively so that he can prevent the possibility of behaving in a socially undesirable way. He quells the threat of his own emotions by being abstract and theoretical.

## Repression

*Repression means that unpleasant, dangerous, and past unfortunate experiences are automatically kept from the person's awareness.* If all such experiences were within one's awareness, it would be impossible for him to exist and function properly without feeling anxious and miserable. Repression is considered as one of the most basic defense mechanisms. Feelings and thoughts which are threatening to one's integrity, as well as intolerable and unacceptable urges, are kept away from his conscious mind, so that he is protected from them. Furthermore, thoughts that are apt to arouse shame and guilt, feelings that may bring on failure, and the expression of hostile impulses and unacceptable drives are most likely to be repressed so that the person may feel more comfortable with himself. The following case is an example of repression.

> Ann cannot prolong a friendship with any boy in college. As soon as she becomes emotionally close to someone, she spontaneously develops a hostile attitude and she rejects him. She does not know why she gets "cold feet," nor the reasons for developing a negative attitude toward males. In reality, Ann was never close to her father, because at an early age when she had been clinging and dependent upon him, he did not understand her needs and he ignored her feelings. As a result, Ann, while still desiring to form a close relationship with a male, suddenly breaks away from the person she really needs, even if he has never given her any indication that he will reject her. Ann repressed her feelings and experiences of fear which were associated with being rejected by her father, and this is why she unknowingly separates herself from a relationship which she consciously desires. The repressed fear of rejection steers away from forming close emotional ties with men.

### Resistance

*Resistance is an automatic force which prevents unpleasant and painful repressed contents in the unconscious part of the mind to enter the conscious part.* Resistance is closely linked to the process of repression, since it prevents the release of repressed material. Resistance takes place when one is being probed about his personality, motives, needs, etc., and it prevents him from facing himself as he is because he may feel socially unacceptable, anxious, guilty, or shameful. Typical examples of resistance would be the student's blocking, long silences, changing the topic of conversation, not understanding what is being asked from him, periods of embarrassment when faced with situations which are threatening to his self-esteem, such as having to talk to a dean or a girlfriend about unacceptable conduct. Students often show resistance when they are expected to talk about themselves, as exemplified in the case below.

> Paula had difficulty making friends in her dorm, and she

was mostly withdrawn and shy with her roommates. The dean invited Paula to his office and encouraged her to vent her feelings about the other girls. Paula was very reluctant to express herself. She made a passing comment about the furniture and she became preoccupied with reading the dean's degrees and credentials which were hanging on the wall. When the dean attempted again to have her talk about her feelings, she looked at the nearby newspaper and commented on the headlines about the disarmament talks. After a long silence, she nervously opened her French text, and after looking at a page for a moment she began talking about the use of the French language in the United Nations. Paula was repelling the dean's attempts to get her to talk about herself. By opposing the dean's efforts, she prevented him from learning things about herself which may have been uncomplimentary or embarrassing.

## Suppression

*Suppression implies that the person holds back or "forgets" unpleasant and unacceptable feelings and thoughts which are not socially condoned, and are threatening to him.* This mechanism is similar to repression in that an unacceptable feeling or thought is pushed out of one's awareness. But with suppression he does this deliberately; whereas, repression takes place without a conscious effort. Thus, unacceptable desires and thoughts are consciously not expressed. In other words, he restrains himself from expressing what society does not allow. For example, when one is angry he can control his expression of anger by deliberately withholding it, and by pressing his lips, although inside he feels hostile and tense. The student who feels abused by his date becomes unusually silent and withdrawn during the evening, although he really experiences anger. From the following example, one can easily understand how useful suppression can be for the student.

Sue's boyfriend became angry at her because in his opinion, she had failed to pay enough attention to him in social situations. As he was describing to her the details of her behavior, which was a very annoying procedure, she swallowed her pride and refused to argue back at him. Instead, she looked at him straight in the eyes, listened to him sympathetically, and did not display any sort of emotion although she actually felt as angry as he did. Sue avoided further conflict and embarrassment by withholding her real feelings toward her boyfriend for making such demands on her.

## Identification

*Identification means that one develops emotional ties with another person, and he acts and behaves as if he were this other person.* Students often imitate by making the same gestures, using the same phrases, or even reproducing the same tone of voice as those of their instructors and other important figures in their lives that they happen to admire and respect. Aligning and identifying oneself with important figures who have shown excellence and accomplishment is a healthy way for a student to integrate himself and to give more meaning to his actions. This process gives the student a sense of direction; when he feels he is accomplishing something on his own merit, his identification with his task becomes stronger. Many important persons began their careers this way until they reached their goals and became fully identified with a profession, a group, trade, etc. This process of identification should not be interpreted as a sign of weakness or some sort of dependency, but should be accepted as a stimulus for personal growth.

The student acquires a feeling of security and strength when he identifies with people or groups. As he patterns himself after persons whom he esteems, or takes part in high ideals and causes, he becomes part of them to the point where he may experience distress when these persons or ideals are being rejected or destroyed. Since he feels a sense of being one with them, he experiences the same feelings that he thinks they might experience. Like most defense mechanisms, the process of identification is largely unconscious. When the student admires someone and tries to take on his characteristics and desirable personal qualities, he is not aware that he is identifying with this person. Of course, identification can be for persons, groups, and ideals which are not socially approved (gangs, outlaws, radical ideals). Below is an example of identification which is harmful rather than helpful.

Joan was elected queen of her high school because of her physical beauty and popularity. Everyone admired and was very kind to her. As a result, she did not have to go out of her way to make friends or study seriously. Everything was given to her without any effort coming from herself. She never took seriously any worthwhile goals in life, such as education, religion, vocation, etc. She wanted only to major in the theatre arts, and she adopted many characteristics of actresses, thinking that she was one herself. She liked to imitate the gait, gestures, and bodily mannerisms of the actresses she admired. She was even successful in adopting the voice of a particular actress she admired. Her dates were mainly attracted by her physical appearance; however, it did not take long for them to realize that mentally and emotionally she had very little to give, and that she always thought of herself first but never wanted to understand other people. She dated handsome men exclusively, because the actresses she admired dated the same type of men. Joan did not realize that her identification with actresses was doing her harm both personally and socially.

## Introjection

*Introjection is the adoption of values and aims of others into one's own personality.* This process is often part of the operation of identification. By introjection, the person internalizes into his own personality the standards and goals of other people, so that he behaves as if these traits were coming entirely from himself. Many students adopt or incorporate aims and standards of other important and admirable persons, and by doing this they increase their self-worth, and do not feel different and isolated. The student whose advisor has a great deal of self-esteem is introjecting his advisor's characteristics if he likes to wear the same type of clothes and to smoke the identical brand of pipe mixture. By embodying these personal tastes and interests, he enhances his own self-esteem. The case below is a good example.

Dave's father was a successful small manufacturer who wanted Dave to succeed him in his business. Dave always wished to be a high school teacher, but his father thought of this idea as being "strictly nonsense." Dave felt quite uncomfortable whenever he mentioned to his father anything that had to do with teaching. But the minute he began to show an interest in his father's business, he felt accepted and appreciated by him. Finally, Dave resolved the problem with his father by changing into the business administration curriculum, where he already had shown sufficient aptitude. By incorporating into his personality his father's values and aspirations, he reduced the threat and the fear of being rejected by his father.

## Reaction-formation

*Reaction-formation is the device whereby a person behaves and expresses himself in a manner which is precisely the opposite of what he really feels like saying or doing.* If he acted as he actually felt, his behavior could be socially unacceptable and he might get into difficulty. The mechanism of reaction-formation is quite useful because it enables the person to face some of his problems with less difficulty by keeping in check his impulses and socially intolerable thoughts. Many a student has been kind and interested in other students, for example, when he really felt hostile toward them. Another frequent example is that of the student who fails an exam and approaches his instructor with an overly polite and charming manner, although in reality he is angry. The next situation is very typical.

Andy was arranged with a blind date. When the prospective girl was pointed out to him from a distance by his friends, he became angry and outraged because she did not meet with his expectations. However, if he expressed what he really felt about her, he would have acted immaturely and he would have embarrassed his friends. As he shook hands with the girl he became cheerful, very polite, and he showed understanding toward her. Toward the end of the evening he complimented her, and he went out of his way to express his thankfulness for the unforgettable evening he had spent with her. He was thus able to control his hostile impulses. By being kindly and cooperative he concealed his real hostile feelings toward his date which are not socially condoned.

## Sublimation

*Sublimation is the process of channellizing conventionally unacceptable drives into activities that are socially approved and desirable.* It is a process through which sexual and aggressive urges, particularly, are transformed and directed into channels of activity which promote the welfare of society and of the individual. Sublimation is considered to be one of the healthiest of mental mechanisms. There are many examples whereby sexual and aggressive drives are converted into approved and accepted behavior. The boy who was raised in a tough neighborhood and has learned to engage in fights, becomes a successful boxer. The frustrated, unmarried school teacher writes short stories expressing subtle sexual content, disguised beneath the talent of her literary creativity. Below is an example of sublimation.

> Nick was a very active, outgoing, and socially rebellious boy in high school. He had been a leader of a gang which committed a variety of delinquent acts (thievery, vandalism, sexual promiscuity). In college, he apparently realized that he could never function as a student if his rebelliousness continued. During his first year in college, he somehow developed an interest in becoming a probation officer, after he had taken a course in criminology. He felt that this field would be very exciting to him, since he already had some experience from his own behavior. By being a probation officer he would still be dealing with delinquents, but in a different relationship altogether. Although Nick is still considered aggressive, his socially disapproved drive is now redirected into a responsible, socially integrated, and useful channel of expression which protects society.

## Rationalization

*Rationalization is the mental mechanism whereby one gives a plausible or "better" reason to justify his acts or ideas, which are actually based on altogether different but real reasons not acceptable to him.* With this device the student makes excuses for his failures and for many acts which do not appear favorable for his self-esteem. Rationalization is a very common mechanism and is used quite frequently by students. The student who shows undesirable behavior (cheating, drinking, laziness, studying just enough to get by) may attempt to make such behavior sound reasonable and justified and gain social approval by telling everyone that "everybody else is doing the same thing anyway." Below is a typical example.

Tom had called a few girls to arrange a week-end date and was refused. After some disappointment and a feeling that perhaps, girls did not care for him very much, or that he was not attractive to them physically, he returned to his residence and announced to his roommates that he would stay in all week-end because he had to prepare a paper to hand in on Monday, and that he had to study for a quiz for the following Tuesday. Obviously, these were not the *real* reasons for his staying in and studying, and for not dating that week-end. However, these reasons were more acceptable to himself and to his friends. It was easier for him to make use of this excuse than to admit his feelings of having been rejected and humiliated by the girls.

Nearly everyone is familiar with the attitude that if one cannot achieve the goal he desires, he concludes that he never wanted that goal in the first place. Aesop's fable of the fox who could not reach the grapes because they were too high and concluded that they were sour, is the best example of rationalization. The person who rationalizes is actually fooling himself, because he never accepts his real limitations; instead, he unconsciously fabricates a more "logical" reason for his actions which protects him from those negative traits which reflect an unfavorable evaluation of himself. Thus, the student who fails to attain a sufficient grade point average for graduate studies may conclude that the time and money required for the advanced degree is not really worth the effort, and that practical, on-the-job experience is more important in the long run.

### Devaluation

*Devaluation is another form of rationalization, through which the person minimizes the importance of an event or condition, so that it becomes less threatening and less anxiety provoking to him.* The student who receives a low grade in a course can feel more comfortable about it when he says to himself that the course has no real purpose in his curriculum, and that what he learned in it will never be useful to him. The girl who was rejected by her date can say to herself that his vocational aspirations were very low, and that he was not much of husband material for her. Thus, the student prefers to "believe" that the goal was not worth attaining, rather than to admit that he simply failed to reach the goal. An example of devaluation follows.

Although Judy was selected among the finalists at a beauty queen contest, she failed to win. Consequently, she declared that beauty is only "skin deep," and that "brains are what really count." She felt that it is superficial to seek out others merely on the basis of physical appearance, and that beauty contests ought to be abolished because they emphasize wrong and misleading values. In fact, she was glad she did not win in the contest, because now she could have more respect for herself, and people should admire her for her personality rather than her physical appearance. Finally, Judy developed a feeling of contempt toward any girl who aspired to enter a beauty contest, and she belittled other attractive girls.

## Denial

*Denial is the refusal to accept a fact as being an actual threat to the individual.* With this device, the person protects himself from the danger of the real problem by his unwillingness to accept it as threatening or unpleasant to him. He refuses to believe that something noxious or unfortunate is taking place, when in reality it actually exists. Denial is a special form of rationalization. The student who was rejected by his girlfriend, or who received an uncomplimentary grade may go on for several days refusing to admit to himself that these events really happened to him. He deceives himself by pretending that nothing harmful actually occurred, and he continues to function as if nothing actually happened. If he did admit these events to himself, he would become anxious and unhappy. Below is a typical example of denying a real threat.

Ron is scheduled for his prelims but he is not too concerned with the ordeal of having to face a panel of professors, and answer difficult questions. He says that the members have known him from having taken courses with them in the past, that they have always liked him, and that there is no reason why he should have any fears that they will fail him. He claims that his professors are basically understanding persons who are there to help rather than to reject him. For this reason, he does not feel he should study intensively, nor should he worry about his prelims. Thus, Ron minimizes the threat simply by denying that such a threat exists, so that he experiences little anxiety or distress over his scheduled prelims. When the safeguard of denial is as strong as described above, it may result in failure.

## Restitution

*Restitution is the relieving of guilt and anxiety caused by having acted against one's moral code, through making amends and reparations for such acts.* Restitution can be a more or less conscious device, and it can involve contrition and repentance. There is often a conscious element of regret for having made transgressions which spurs the person to make up for his wrong-doings by penitence and by actions from which others derive benefit. The student who, years ago, took out a book from the college library without returning it, and who upon graduation makes a small donation to the library fund, is an example of restitution. This mechanism is workable and often effective for the student who has violated his moral standards, and who is motivated to take constructive action to eliminate the guilt and anxiety which he may experience. The following example clarifies this point.

Don feels guilty for having gone sexually "too far" with his girl. Although he talked the matter over with his religious advisor, he could not find relief and peace with himself. He began to make restitution for his act by treating his girl with extreme courtesy, he made it a point to be in early every evening, he attended church regularly, and he enrolled in a course in religion. His social conduct in college became exemplary as he transformed himself into a model student. He participated in various student organizations and he impressed his advisor so favorably with his impeccable moral conduct and with his trustfulness that he was eventually appointed a counselor for freshman students, and he even chaperoned their dances! Don made amends for having violated his moral code by becoming an ideal student through *redemptive and purposeful activity.*

The mechanism of restitution has produced many great men throughout the history of mankind. St. Augustine is a vivid example. Although during his youth he had been prodigal, in later life he restored himself through his writings which inspired and elevated the early Christian Church to new heights. His life was transformed through his creativity in spiritual and intellectual works. King David in the Old Testament is another example. After having violated the moral law, he became severely depressed, and he began his restitution by expressing his repentance and faith in his famous psalms. Likewise, many persons have attained sainthood in the Christian Church by denouncing their sins, by gaining new self-insights, and by performing outstanding deeds. From the foregoing, the student can understand the powerful effect of active restitution, and how this mechanism can help him overcome his anxieties and guilt.

## Displacement

*Displacement is the transfer of an unacceptable feeling or thought from the person or situation which aroused it, to another unrelated person or situation.* The reason for this transfer is that if the person behaved as he really felt toward the source of his feelings and thoughts, he may suffer undesirable consequences which may cause him to become anxious. If a student, for example, were angry toward his professor for having failed an exam, he would not dare express his feelings to the professor, the real source of his feelings. With the mechanism of displacement, he can unload his unacceptable feelings on someone else, such as his roommate, where the consequences may not be as severe. Thus, the student finds relief as he expresses his anger and pent-up feelings of hostility on someone who is less likely to be dangerous or who would reject or think less of him. Below is an example of displacement.

Ann did not want to return to college because she was failing. However, she had not been able to convince her

mother of this, with the result that she developed strong negative feelings toward her mother who was encouraging her to
return to college. Ann returned to the campus very reluctantly,
and in her first class session she disagreed, on a minor point,
with her instructor who was about the same age as Ann's
mother. Ann was visibly so irritated in class that the instructor
asked her to come into her office after class for an explanation
of her feelings. She intimated that the instructor had been
stubborn, demanding, and inconsiderate of other people's
feelings. Although Ann was not aware of it, she was simply
transferring her feelings over her mother to her instructor.
In her case, the instructor was not as threatening to her as her
mother, because Ann was not highly motivated to attend
college in the first place.

## Projection

*Projection is the mental mechanism whereby the individual
sees or senses undesirable personal characteristics, thoughts, attitudes, etc. in other persons or groups which are already typical
of himself and of which he may not be fully aware.* If an
individual were unable to use this mechanism occasionally, he
would constantly have to face those faults and shortcomings
of his own which make him feel uncomfortable and anxious.
Thus, he relieves his anxiety and personal discomfort by projecting his weaknesses unto other persons or groups as a protection
against admitting to himself his own deficiencies. He attributes
to them what he may not be willing to accept in himself. Sometimes, one's strong points are projected unto others, i.e., he may
see only the good things in other people. This process makes him
feel accepted by them, and they may eventually overlook or
tolerate his weaknesses.

A student may feel that other students do not like him or
that they think unfavorably of him, yet, those others may not
actually think this way. Rather than admitting that he himself
has such thoughts over his own low self-esteem, it becomes
more convenient for him to attribute these thoughts as coming
from others. This student obviously relieves his felt guilt about
his failures or his deficiencies in his personality by talking about
other students' faults and transgressions. The same can be said

about groups. For example, when a student has not been able to make himself acceptable to a particular group in college, he may resent and hate the group; but rather than admitting these feelings as being part of himself, he may blame the group as being hostile toward him. When his own feelings are projected as coming from the group, he is relieved of them. In other words, he perceives the whole situation in reverse because this way it is more tolerable to him.

The mechanism of projection operates widely in all people, in varying degrees and often without one being aware of it. It is difficult for one to avoid projecting. Simple comments or casual descriptions of people and even of objects can contain personal projections. The way we feel and think about the world can reflect our own needs and characteristics. The way we perceive the objective world often reveals our inner, subjective world. The writer, for example, who at his very old age writes vividly about the "old, forgotten, and lonely violin in the cold and barren attic, covered with dust, dried-up and cracked, and with broken strings and the lustre gone" is most likely describing himself. Likewise, the unmotivated student who receives low grades and who describes his instructors as being "dull and disorganized" in class, is probably ascribing to them his own self-image. An example of projection follows.

Mary is a fairly attractive student who is unreasonably shy and withdrawn. As a young girl, she was criticized by her strict parents, who had prevented her from participating in social groups from fear that she may get into "trouble." She was not allowed to be herself in the house, she was scolded whenever she spoke her mind, and her parents wanted to plan her whole life. As a result, she felt inadequate and inferior in college, and she harbored a poor image of herself, socially and academically. She never learned to express herself, and to feel that she belonged in college. She withdrew from other people because she felt they were "phoney" and "empty," and that they would criticize her should she ever express her real feelings. She sensed negative feelings toward herself as coming from others, rather than from herself. Therefore, **they** were to blame for her shyness and social sensitivity. She felt that **others** thought she was inadequate and inferior and avoided her for these reasons, when in reality this was the way she thought about herself but could not accept it.

## Regression

*Regression is the reverting to a chronologically earlier phase of behavior which is characteristic of less mature functioning.* When a person is under stress, he can ward off the anxiety by acting in a manner which is not consistent with his present age. By acting childishly, he can handle the presence of threat and difficulty. For example, the student who feels uncomfortable and inadequate in social situations may "clown" and go out of his way to be funny in order to conceal his tenseness. The female student who has difficulty with parents or boyfriends may gain attention and be taken care of by her roommates with "baby-talk," or with crying over irrelevant matters. By reverting to less mature behavior, the student feels absolved from the responsibility that the present situation may demand of him. Below, a case of regressive behavior is described.

Diane is a graduate student who had been crying in her dorm because her boyfriend left her. She felt totally helpless and unable to control her feelings. When Diane went to see a counselor on the floor, she appeared with blue jeans, a sweat shirt, long pony-tail hairdo, and gym shoes, and she chewed gum noisily. She laughed and giggled, and she hopped as she entered the counselor's office. Diane did not show the sophistication expected of a woman her age. When the counselor pointed out her inappropriate behavior, Diane broke into tears. In other words, when Diane was confronted with a trying situation, she reverted to a behavior pattern which she had exhibited in the past, because it was more comfortable to her. By acting like a little girl, by crying and sulking, she retreated into a situation which was easier for her to cope with.

Those who are more prone to regress to childish behavior when faced with difficulties are those who have been dependent on parents or other strong figures. Basically, such persons lack confidence and feel that they cannot take care of themselves when having to relate responsibly to the adult world. Thus, when they cannot succeed in life and achieve goals in a conventional manner they act in an immature fashion (pouting, raising their voice, crying, making childish demands, stubbornness, silly laughter, and generally acting like a child) whereby they hope to be and many times succeed in being taken care of. In other words, their actions compel others to treat them as children and, therefore, little or no demands are made of them.

## Malingering

*Malingering is the deliberate feigning of physical symptoms in order to avoid an unpleasant situation which produces anxiety.* The student invents physical symptoms, or pretends to be ill, in order to excuse himself from something threatening, fearsome, anxiety-provoking, etc. Unlike the other adjustment mechanisms, malingering is *consciously* fabricated by the person. He is well aware of what he is doing, and he knows what he expects to gain. The malingering student does not experience physical pain; he is simply being deceitful in order to get out of an undesirable situation. Malingering reflects a certain amount of immaturity and passivity on the student and, in the long run, it is a very poor and ineffective way to cope with undesirable situations. The fear and humiliation of being discovered, along with guilt, may become an additional burden to the student, and even more painful than the situation he wants to escape. A typical case follows.

Dorothy is unprepared for her final exams; however, she has always been able to manipulate people and to get out of an unpleasant task by feigning illness. In the past she missed many classes, and, as a child, she derived a great deal of attention whenever she complained of feeling "sick." On the day of her first exam she woke up too late to go to class. She immediately went to the college dispensary complaining of "illness," but the physician found nothing wrong with her. Meanwhile, she attempted to be excused from her exam and to have it postponed to a more convenient date. Dorothy felt very perplexed and embarrassed when the dean inquired why she did not report to the dispensary when she had been "ill" during the semester. Her trick of malingering had been exposed, and had finally come to an end.

❖    ❖    ❖    ❖

The following four mechanisms of defense, although normal if manifested in mild degrees, may be considered malignant if found in exaggerated forms. The more severe forms of these mechanisms, however, are quite rare phenomena, although mild manifestations of them do occasionally occur among college students without causing them excessive distress, or becoming a real problem for them that would necessitate treatment.

## Phobia

*Phobia is an irrational, morbid, and strong fear of a situation, object, idea, act, or person which is symbolically and remotely associated with the real source of dread.* In many instances the origin of the association cannot be fully established. While mild fears are normal, strong and persistent phobias over things which are quite harmless may require psychiatric consultation. Typical phobias are those of high, open, or closed places, of certain animals, diseases, special objects, etc. In these cases, the real fear originates from something else which the person *cannot* avoid; hence, the fear becomes focused on something harmless which *can* be readily avoided. For example, if a student dreads the anticipation of academic failure from which he cannot escape, he can develop a distressing fear of crowded rooms which he can avoid. He transfers his fear from the real source (threat of failure) to a potentially harmless situation (the classroom). The example below illustrates a case of phobia.

Peter has excessive fear of dogs, of darkness, and when someone accidentally happens to be walking behind him. He complains of no other significant problems. Peter is able to avoid the darkness and dogs, so that only in a few instances he feels intense fear. He experiences no symptoms of fear when friends happen to be with him. Peter's phobias are not severe enough to require treatment, since he is able to maneuver around them. It would probably require long term treatment for him to uncover the real source of phobia. However, if these phobias were severe enough to cause him immense anxiety in his social functioning, then professional help would be required and desirable.

## Obsession-Compulsion

*Obsessive-compulsive behavior is characteristic of repetitive acts and persistent throughts which the person cannot control, and which appear irrational and morbid.* The person feels compelled to do or think things which do not make much sense to him. Everyone has mild obsessions and compulsions which occur periodically and are not necessarily harmful to him. The student who must take a shower, straighten out his bookcase, and shine his shoes before he can settle in his studies still remains fairly efficient as a student; in fact, they may even be useful to him. But if the student, during the course of the day, has to wash his hands immediately after he touches anything, even his books and pencils, such a compulsion may become burdensome and incapacitating. The following case illustrates the pathological type of obsessive-compulsive behavior.

> When Harold sees violence on television or when he reads about a crime in the papers, he experiences recurrent thoughts that he will harm someone. He is afraid to touch a knife or other instruments with which he could harm others. The result is that he is tense when he is with other people. Harold is also nervous when he is about to study; he cannot get down to work unless he spends hours reading a booklet titled **How to Study.** After this, he spends more time arranging the furniture, the lighting, the books, etc. But when he has performed all this ritual and is about ready to open the books, the thoughts that he will harm someone return. Thus, he cannot study and he is failing in college. Although many students, at times, experience these symptoms in a small degree, in the case of Harold they prevent him from functioning normally, and professional treatment would be recommended in this case.

It is believed that obsessions and compulsions are exaggerated forms for making symbolic self-amends. The compulsion to wash the hands may be an attempt to cleanse oneself from guilt in order to counteract a real or imagined immoral act, or, the obsession that he will harm the person he loves may be his means of stifling socially aggressive and sexual impulses. In both cases there is a certain amount of security involved, as these defenses serve as controlling agents. By washing the hands he is symbolically undoing an unacceptable act, and by entertaining obsessional thoughts he transforms the socially unacceptable impulsive act into a haunting idea, and prevents it from becoming a reality.

## Conversion

*Conversion is the removal of anxiety by discharging it into physical symptoms, which occur in those parts of the body over which the person has conscious control* (talking, walking, moving the hands, seeing, etc.). These symptoms occur in the muscles and the sensory organs, and are excluded from those parts of the body which are under control of the autonomic nervous system (respiration, digestion, elimination, heart, etc.). Conversion symptoms either involve a paralysis of the muscle, or the inability of the sensory organ to function properly. Actually, the organ or muscle is not really damaged, despite the fact that the accompanying pain or paralysis is real. Anxiety over an emotional conflict is *converted* into a physical symptom which, in turn, helps the person out of a threatening situation.

Students occasionally demonstrate examples of conversion symptoms. The voice major who is about to give her senior recital "loses" her voice as soon as she is to begin singing. The graduate student who plans to take his written prelims develops a mild paralysis in the right hand (writer's cramps). The athlete just before a track meet suddenly cannot move his feet, as if they were paralysed. In all these situations a threat of failure in these tasks creates anxiety, and this anxiety is displaced or diverted into these parts of the body so that they do not function well. The result is that the person can avoid or be excused from the threatening situation which requires the services of these organs or muscles. The following case illustrates a conversion symptom.

> Arlene became secretly engaged to a student of whom her parents had disapproved. Although she wanted to postpone the marriage, she finally conceded to marrying him despite her reservations. The day the marriage was to take place, she was unable to get out of bed and stand on her feet. She felt a lack of equilibrium, and the floor seemed to her "spongy" and "revolving." She felt that her feet were paralyzed and "waxy." Although there was nothing physically wrong with her,

the ceremony was postponed. The anxiety Arlene felt for becoming married without her parents' knowledge was spontaneously channelled into a specific part of her body that served the purpose of delaying the marriage by becoming an invalid. By this means, she temporarily alleviated her anxiety over her uncertainty of marriage.

## Dissociation

*Dissociation is the process whereby one's personality becomes temporarily disorganized so that his mental functions are separated, and his personal identity is lost from consciousness.* By not knowing who he is one solves his current problem and lessens the anxiety which such a problem or conflict may produce. This phenomenon is typical of the person who is described in the news items as suffering from amnesia, i.e., one who does not know his name, where he is at the moment, what he does for a living, or where he lives. By dissociating himself from the past, and by becoming *depersonalized*, he loses his feeling of self-identity and finds temporary relief from an anxiety-producing crisis. The onset and remission of dissociated states is usually sudden. Sleepwalking, multiple personalities, fugues, and various sleep-like states also belong in this category. A typical dissociation is shown in the case below.

> For a year, Ellen had been steadily dating a man whom she was eventually going to marry. While he was away for a while, she was casually introduced to another man with whom she became strongly infatuated. As she dated him a few times, she became tense and anxious, causing her physical attraction toward him to become stronger. One morning Ellen woke up without being able to remember the man's name, appearance, what he had been saying to her, or where they had been the previous evening. All she could recall was a vague notion that she had met someone. Ellen felt guilty of her sexual attraction toward a person she did not intend to marry, since she was already committed to someone else. The mental mechanism of dissociation made her segregate or disconnect him temporarily from her mind in order to reduce the conflict.

     ✿    ✿    ✿    ✿

Every student employs several of these mechanisms in order

to minimize some of his anxiety about his shortcomings. As long as his efficiency as a student and as a social participant is not markedly reduced, he need not have fears for using these mechanisms. For him to have identified some of these devices in himself and to realize that other students, who are just as normal as he, have the same experiences with these mechanisms, are definitely signs of normality and of having a healthy mind. Consequently, the less mentally sound the student becomes, the less he is able to recognize these defenses in himself.

# 5

## TYPICAL SYMPTOMS IN THE
## COLLEGE STUDENT

COLLEGE STUDENTS APPROACH counselors with many different symptoms, and it is a difficult task for the counselor to determine the nature of the maladjustment from the particular symptom that they present. Any one area of maladjustment in the college student will not always produce the same symptoms. Students who encounter difficulty with studying and concentrating on their work, for example, report different symptoms associated with their inability to study. The experience of the personnel, in most mental hygiene services in colleges and universities, indicates that there are three major symptoms of maladjustment in college: anxiety, depression, and physical complaints based on a psychological problem. Sometimes, all three symptoms are present in varying degrees in the same student, and they are regularly found to a small degree in *every* student. Stress rising from within the student or from the environment which is not adequately handled or discharged may cause any or all of these symptoms to a disabling degree.

There are certain terms widely used among clinicians which the student of mental health should know. A *chronic* symptom is one that appears slowly and persists for a long time; an *acute* symptom appears suddenly. Identification of the nature or type of an emotional disorder is referred to as a *diagnosis*. Usually the *prognosis* is simultaneously made, whereby the outcome, and the duration of the disorder is estimated. *Symptom* refers to the characteristic changes of behavior (thinking, feeling) that indicate the presence of an emotional disorder, and *syndrome* denotes a group of symptoms that make up the characteristics of a particular emotional difficulty. Finally, *etiology* signifies the causes that are responsible for an existing mental condition.

Mental and emotional problems can be either *functional* or *organic* in nature. By the term *functional* we mean any disorder, conflict, or pattern of behavior which is essentially of a mental nature, or, negatively stated, where there are no organic conditions which underlie the disturbance. It is the function, not the structure, which is affected. The term *organic* refers to the body, and it implies changes in the physical structure of the nervous system. Its impairment may be of considerable importance in the cause of a mental symptom, as in cerebral arteriosclerosis, brain damage, syphilis, glandular disturbances, alcoholism, and cancer.

As noted earlier, *maladjustment* implies the inability to solve the problems of living and to satisfy adequately one's psychological needs; however, the majority of students who experience some type of emotional difficulty and require professional help are not mentally ill in the true sense of the word. The study and prevention of emotional disorders is the task of psychiatry and abnormal psychology. Although there is no one theory that explains all aberrant behavior, psychologists and psychiatrists have adequate knowledge to understand them and to offer remedial assistance. There are different schools of thought regarding the cause and cure of emotional problems, but there is general agreement concerning the various types of these problems. The following pages will present the major types of emotional problems as seen from the point of view of the personnel in mental hygiene in colleges and universities.

## The Meaning of Anxiety

Anxiety is best understood as a mental and/or physical state of agitation, restlessness, and nervous discontent, which is mostly due to a painful suspense of an unknown or vague anticipatory danger. Commonly known as "nerves," anxiety is felt as apprehension, uneasiness, and occasionally as a sensation of panic. It is manifested through physical symptoms: perspiration in the palms and upper lip, muscle tenseness, rapid heartbeat, a pounding sensation in the head, dilation of the pupils of the eye, and a keen attention alternating with occasional periods of mental confusion. Anxiety affects the student's emotions and thought processes which in turn can impede his academic work, depending upon the degree of intensity. Tension is often relieved when the student is given the opportunity to talk out the problems that are producing the anxiety, identify them, and learn to take more constructive steps in solving them.

Although *mild* anxiety is one of the most common symptoms in a student, its effects become undesirable when the anxiety symptoms are too prolonged and severe, and when he cannot identify the underlying reason. While some of the causes are temporary and superficial, as when the student is confronted with a real threat (imminent rejection and failure), many of them are deep seated and of long duration, even though he may be performing quite well academically and socially. Anxiety is not a characteristic that stands by itself; it is a symptom generated by a cause. Normally, mild anxiety does not require medical or psychiatric intervention. Students who feel mild anxiety may not be too concerned with the underlying conflicts; they can accept them as normal consequences of the pressure of college. The reason for this is clear. Anxiety is nature's way to protect the individual from threat. If there is real danger which may cause harm to one's life, his nervous system overreacts so that he is quickly mobilized to avoid and to escape from the threat. For example, if a postman discovers a mad dog approaching to attack him, he becomes fearful and he develops the symptoms of acute anxiety. If under these conditions he did not develop such reactions, his life would be in jeopardy. Therefore, anxiety serves a purpose when it is directly related to a potentially harmful situation. When the danger is gone, normally the symptoms also disappear.

The same reactions, but without the immediate causes, are frequently experienced by the college student. Very often, students complain of anxiety without being able to identify any specific problem or any sizable threat in their environment. They are unaware of any potential danger sign; yet, the symptoms of anxiety are as strong as if a threat were actually present. In most of these cases, the threat is *psychological*. Anxiety, or any kind of mental or physical symptom, does not come on by itself; there must be an antecedent condition associated with it. There can be many underlying unconscious factors that cause the student to be anxious. Tension can be the result of pent-up hostile feelings toward parents, the opposite sex, or toward the student himself for not being able to live up to his ideals. Often, concern over the future and the consequences that he anticipates can cause him to experience anxiety at any one moment. Anxiety can increase to the point where he feels he is ready to "explode." Any of the unresolved conflicts presented and discussed in Chapters 2 and 3 can be associated with his anxiety.

A moderate amount of anxiety in the student is very useful and beneficial, because it keeps him alert and vigilant. Before an exam, for example, a little anxiety keeps the student "tuned-up" and in a state of readiness to respond to the challenge. Furthermore, he shows concern and eagerness to excel. This is, obviously, a healthy condition for the student who desires to succeed; anxiety can be a source of energy which is at his disposal for mobilizing him and for serving his needs. If the student did not worry, nor experience any anxiety at all, he would be prone to appear apathetic, and to show little interest in his work; he would be lackadaisical and unconcerned. On the other hand, excessive anxiety and worry can incapacitate him. For example, in the exam if he "freezes up" or "blocks," his mind becomes temporarily impaired. But as the anxiety subsides, he is able to function again, thus able to recall more material as the examination time progresses.

Anxiety is often the result of the student's difficulty in accomplishing the tasks that either he or society expects of him. Specifically, when there is a clash between the student's inability to perform or avoid a particular act on the one hand, and those tasks which society wants him to perform or avoid on the other, he frequently develops anxiety. Furthermore, anxiety can stem from a feeling of being incapable of meeting the requirements of parents, teachers, peers, society, etc., thus failing to win their approval and acceptance, or to prevent the loss of self-esteem.

Also, it can originate from the student's own failure to fulfill his goals, or from guilt of having violated society's standards. Finally, it can serve as a danger signal signifying that his integrity is being threatened.

When the student anticipates defeat, he tends to consider himself unwanted and unfit to be in college, and he can become hostile and aggressive. These negative feelings may make him feel anxious because they are not considered acceptable in college. Thus, anxiety in the student may be related to the awareness of his own feelings of hostility coming toward the surface. Anxiety may also be produced by pressure, criticism, or ridicule from parents, peers and siblings which he wards off by expressing hostility. As is often common with aggressive tendencies, when feelings of hostility are not allowed expression they generate tension. The student can "let off steam" by using socially acceptable ways (debates, athletics).

A sound mind is not the only prerequisite that will guarantee the student's success in college, but also a healthy emotional disposition is needed. The student should realize that if his emotions (hostility, anxiety, depression) are strong or inappropriate, the chances are that he will not be able to produce up to his capacity. When a student is performing mental work, he is more apt to be bothered by these emotions than one who is engaged in physical activities. In fact, the latter may even find relief in such tasks, for every student knows that physical activity relieves tension. If, however, tension goes beyond the degree that is normally expected and makes the student very uncomfortable, then physical activity will be inadequate and other more effective means will have to be instituted.

With respect to mental work, the student's tensions are apt to worsen if no outlet for them is provided. The more he concentrates and worries about them, the more they increase, thus forming a vicious circle. Although the student may be very capable, he may not be able to make the best use of his talents. He feels that something over which he has little control is holding him back.

The causes of anxiety may not be too clear to the student. Such causes as hostility and resentment toward those who are pressuring him, conflict with peers because of an unresolved rivalry with a sibling, having a poor image of himself, and inability to relate to authority, which is often the outgrowth of disturbed relationships with punitive parents, are likely to be present. As with many types of undesirable behavior, it must be emphasized that there is not always a single, definite, clear-cut cause for every case with anxiety symptoms. Just as in the physical illnesses, the physician cannot make a diagnosis by knowing the degree of fever alone, since high temperature is but one symptom in a large number of illnesses. The same applies to the psychological symptoms of anxiety.

The onset of anxiety is difficult to predict. It can appear at the time when the student anticipates or is beginning to study, during participation in athletic activities, or when he is engaged in an activity unrelated to college. This tension or restlessness is often directly related to these tasks, either because of unfortunate experiences having been attached to them from the past due to mixed feelings and doubts over the outcome of a particular activity, or because of fear of failure, or a host of different emotional attitudes. Some students become more anxious over their concern for their anxiety; the more they worry about their anxiety the more anxious they become. The cycle can be disrupted if the student changes his attitude toward his anxiety symptoms, as happened in the following example of an anxiety problem for which a student sought help.

A student majoring in Music Education complained of being unhappy, nervous, perplexed and of becoming tense when he was around people. There was a quaver in his voice, some jitteriness in his hands, and he seemed as if he was ready to burst into tears. He told of having very few friends, and of deriving very little excitement from life. He admitted having frequent daydreams, and he referred to himself as a "hermit." He felt very cautious toward his girlfriend and experienced fear that she may reject him as she did others before him. He indicated that his most severe problems involved his self-doubt, his worry about certain events and situations, and his adequacy as a marital partner in case he should get married. He stated his lack of conviction that he was in the field best suited for him, and he complained about his difficulty trusting people, including his present girlfriend. Throughout the interview his speech was hesitant and halting.

During therapy, the student was helped to look at himself objectively and to review his personality pattern. He concluded that his apprehension about himself and the future centered around the following questions: "Am I worth anything?" "Will I mean anything to anyone?" "Will anyone need me?" In other words, the mild anxiety he experienced was associated with an unhealthy evaluation of himself, and as he became aware of it, he began to seek the answers which would rectify his faulty self-evaluation. After a few sessions with the psychologist, the student became more active on campus, and by showing greater spontaneity he made more friends. He began to answer questions in class and to feel that his instructors "know I'm there." He became more assertive toward his girlfriend by relinquishing his attitude of self-pity and concentrating more on her own happiness. As he gained more confidence in his interpersonal relationships, he discovered that other students accepted him as a person when he showed social initiative. His doubts dissolved and he became much more relaxed and less self-conscious.

Anxiety in the student is frequently associated with feelings of insecurity over the possibility that he may not survive college. Insecurity is a very common feeling among students. However, it can be a symptom of other, deeper conflicts. The female student can doubt her femininity, for example, and feel insecure in the company of men. Likewise, the male student may sense a lack of strong characteristics typical of his sex, and be reluctant to show interest in the opposite sex, and, although insecurity often originates in childhood, the student can manage to eradicate his feelings of insecurity through meeting with successful experiences in college. Fear of speaking in a group, meeting with new people, etc., despite the student's obvious ability to perform these activities can often be due to a basic sense of insecurity. If the student does not feel safe and confident in his academic work and social life, some mild anxiety can be normally experienced by him.

The student's attempt to forget or not to worry about his symptoms is rarely effective. Although drugs are used in the case of severe symptoms, the most recommended procedure is psychotherapy. The details of method can vary but the main process is to help the student understand the pattern of his personality, and to recognize how he came to react to stress situations with the symptoms that he has. It is not necessary to concentrate on symptoms, but on the causes behind them. Unresolved conflicts with parents, poor identity, fear of expression of emotion, anticipation of failure, too high standards, guilt, loss of reputation, are but few underlying factors. Of course, there are many other reasons for the student's anxiety depending upon his past experiences, and the nature of the present situation. It is always wise for the student with mild anxiety to remain active, and to participate in sports and recreation. Some students can find relief by "using up" their anxiety in physical activity; after a vigorous athletic task many are able to sleep the following evening more comfortably.

Anxiety enables the student to be more adaptive as he is expecting to find anticipated difficulties, rather than to be "caught off guard." Finally, by using the attitude that "everyone feels the same way," prior to a competitive examination, for example, the student can become more capable of tolerating the anxiety with less discomfort and with a minimum of concern with the symptomatic side-effects. Anxiety is often lessened when the student communicates his feelings to his peers and discovers that they feel exactly the same way. Anxiety is not a characteristic of the "weaker" student; it is found equally in the bright and in the "average" student.

In many instances, the student is aware of the conditions that cause his anxiety, such as inability to compete scholastically, avoid failures, find approval through academic success, and numerous others. But there are instances when anxiety cannot be focused on any factor logically associated with his tensions. If the anxiety is mild or even moderate, it may dissipate in a short time.

Up to this point the symptoms of anxiety that were elaborated were either mild or moderate. *Severe* anxiety symptoms (insomnia, tremor, restlessness, loss of appetite, inability to talk) are characteristics which are intense enough to cause the student to become significantly handicapped in his college work for a prolonged period. Under such conditions the student should seek professional help. Of course, students with such acute anxiety symptoms are relatively few compared with those who show mild anxiety. The psychiatrist or physician can dispense drugs and even hospitalize the student, if the symptoms are excessively severe, and if medication and hospitalization are indicated.

## The Meaning of Depression

A feeling of *mild* depression is another common symptom in college students; fortunately, it is also one of the symptoms which has a very good rate of recovery. In most cases, the symptoms dissipate in a few days. The most typical form of depression is that which develops as a reaction to the loss of a loved one in the family—whether real or imagined—as having been rejected by a member of the opposite sex whom the student admired or was dependent upon, and as a failure to meet desired expectations. The usual feelings of depression in the student involve a sense of hopelessness, gloom, forlornness, dejection, and loneliness. These feelings are normal as long as they are not persistent and intensive.

Mild depression is common in many fairly well adjusted students who happen to meet with adverse conditions in college. Experience with students exhibiting mild depressive tendencies indicates that these tendencies are often associated with either academic failure or an unpleasant emotional involvement with the opposite sex. Mild feelings of depression which normally occur in college are not indicative of any abnormality. Feeling "blue" and in the "dumps" on Sunday afternoon (Sunday afternoon neurosis), having "low" spirits during the evenings of the weekend when he is dateless, feeling listless, tired and discouraged are mostly transient experiences and do not label the student as being depressed in the real sense of the word. In a matter of a few hours or a day these feelings vanish. Lack of enthusiasm and sadness can follow an unfortunate and unexpected emotional experience, however, and the following case is a typical example:

A female graduate student had failed in a final examination and requested to see a psychologist because she wanted to "talk to someone." Her gait was slow and her facial expression made her appear to be deeply preoccupied. Her eyes were wet, and she felt as though she were in a "daze." She felt sorry for herself and expressed the desire to be left alone for a while. She was unable to give much information about herself, except that she felt unappreciated, misunderstood, and unwanted, and felt that she was unduly suffering for her failure. She began examining her motives for being in college, took the whole matter of failure as being entirely her own, and came to the conclusion that she was much inferior to other students.

These characteristics described above are normal and appropriate responses to such conditions. After reading the case, one may realize that he himself has encountered similar feelings of mild depression. If the student in the case above had refused to attend classes, stayed in her room for days at a time, lost weight, and spent hours crying and harboring morbid thoughts of self-degradation, then she would have been suffering from a real depression and would require medical attention. The girl in our case responded to encouragement and realized that failure in one course does not necessarily jeopardize one's education. She also came to understand that anyone who is rigid about continuously maintaining high standards will take the "shock" of failure much harder than the student who is less rigid. She returned the following day stating that she was determined to repeat the course. She appeared cheerful and comfortable with herself.

In the majority of students who complain of depression, it is usually mild and can be relieved by talking to someone, and by letting others know how they feel. Much comfort can be achieved by expressing in words how one feels and thinks. Sometimes it is difficult to find a sympathetic audience; but a counselor or a clergyman in the college or the community can be of great help. It is not always necessary that all the reasons for the student's depression be known to him, unless the symptoms are constantly troublesome. As with anxiety, involvement with manual activities and sports can reduce depression, if the student has a moderate amount of physical energy.

The chronically depressed student is a more serious problem. This student finds college life dull and his academic performance vain. He requires more time to absorb material from books, and he derives little gratification from college life. In psychological terms, depression means self-punishment in order to alleviate guilt. Some students blame external conditions for causing their depression and become hostile towards their environment. In many cases social and academic factors are just as responsible as internal conflicts for precipitating depression. Severe and prolonged depression requires therapy and treatment with medication, but milder forms can dissipate in time without therapy, especially if the student has an adaptable personality.

The more *severe* forms of depression can be identified by the student's very gloomy facial expression, slowness of bodily movements, a general neglect of his clothes, and deterioration in his physical appearance. He may sit alone and listless for long periods of time, and he becomes increasingly isolated from his peers. He simply becomes indifferent to what is going on around him, he has a feeling of uselessness, and his morale is very low. Severe depression is also shown by the student's inability to talk, and by his feeling that everything for him has come to a standstill. His roommates and classmates often try to give him "pep" talks, with very meager results. He may harbor suicidal and foreboding thoughts, strong feelings of self-depreciation and guilt, insomnia, early awakening, loss of weight and appetite, mental stagnation, and crying spells which are often without apparent reason.

Depression in its severe form is often looked upon as a reaction to a fear of or actual loss of: (1) a loved person; (2) a desired situation, or (3) self-esteem. However, among college students, depression can be observed which is not clearly tied to any of the above factors. The real cause can run deeper, eventually making it more difficult for the student to understand his depressive symptoms. The fact that depression draws attention to one and makes others show pity, concern, and sympathy is well-known. The depressed student with his morbid preoccupation with self-depreciation will go a long way to convince others how ill he is so that less can be expected of him. By adopting a hopeless attitude toward himself and the future, he depreciates and frustrates the efforts of others who want to help him, and he considers himself not worthy of any attention.

The severely depressed student who suffers from his symptoms is usually directing feelings of hostility or resentment toward another person or persons; people become perturbed and uncomfortable when a close person shows overt evidence of disturbance in mood. In many cases, the depressed student is not aware that he is tyrannizing, manipulating, and gaining mastery and a false sense of superiority over others. In some cases, the depressed student who makes others unhappy by displaying his symptoms may be resenting them for not having loved him. Indeed, for the student who feels he has not been supplied with sufficient love, symptoms of depression can constitute a silent, subtle plea for affection from the world.

Severe symptoms are much less frequent and even rare when compared to the milder features of depression which are more common and more or less normal. Some students who become depressed in college, improve spontaneously without ever seeking help. However, if depressive symptoms persist, there is no reason why such a student should not avail himself of the existing medical facilities. The prognosis for improvement and recovery of the severe state of depression is, in most cases, extremely good.

On rare occasions, college authorities are faced with actual or attempted suicides by students. Suicidal tendencies are found mostly among depressed, and sometimes psychotic and psychopathic students, and, unfortunately, suicide cannot be easily predicted. However, it can be averted in those cases where the student gives serious warning; and with treatment he can face the problem rather than attempt to avoid it by killing himself. Of these students, some are actually responding to an adverse situation by threatening suicide (loss of a loved one), while others are suffering from problems that exist in themselves (guilt, self-hatred). Suicidal attempts in the college population are used as a device to elicit attention and pity, rather than as a drastic means to cause death. The more the student can see that others around him become highly concerned when he threatens suicide, the easier it is for him to continue using this device as a means of controlling them. It is mostly this type of student who usually does not commit the act; he is simply using it as a threat. However, the psychotic who is out of contact with reality, and the psychopathic who is prone to be impulsive and unpredictable, are more likely to commit suicide.

The threat by the depressed student to commit suicide can be an act to revenge someone who has hurt or frustrated him. By attempting to act against his own life, he inevitably hurts others, and he agitates them into such a state that they finally succumb to his wishes for attention. By his suicidal threat, he mobilizes those in his immediate environment through intimidating them and making them feel guilty for not paying much attention to his needs. He exploits their good intentions and he makes them vigilant to his sorrows and failure. Thus, he makes himself the center of attraction, and his needs for love and nurture are being temporarily met. These needs are quite universal and can be satisfied through socially acceptable channels of behavior. The student can gain attention and recognition, and he can feel significant and superior by using means that do not force others into his service.

Just as it can be with anxiety, guilt can sometimes lie at the bottom of depression. Guilt is detected by the way the student depreciates himself, shows excessive concern over his reputation, or tends to act in a self-punishing way. For example, a student may be constantly missing his examinations from oversleeping and be dismissed from college for academic failure. Another may act antisocially (drinking, stealing), but feels "glad" when he is finally apprehended. In both cases he seems to be asking for punishment. At the same time, he is concerned with the idea that if others discovered how he really feels about himself, he would lose all his friends; hence, he seeks self-punishment through isolation and self-pity. During therapy he may be relieved if told what a "bad" person he is. Guilt can be healthy if it spurs the student toward constructive and socially desirable behavior.

Although not always related to sin, guilt in the college setting frequently implies the student's feelings of having omitted or committed an act which was contrary to his conscience, or to the standards of society. Such acts could range from sexual experiences to cheating on exams. The failure of meeting the expectations of parents and of those persons whom the student admires and respects may also create guilt. It can be shown in the form of anxiety as the student becomes aware of his failure to fulfill his ideals and promises, or violates his moral standards. Some students re-examine their real motives for having attended college, and feel guilty for not having done as well as they should. The next case portrays an ideal example of the student who, in his senior year, suddenly realizes he will soon be facing a different world.

A twenty-one-year-old student reported that he was bothered by his attitude about himself. He felt competent but, for no apparent reason, he avoided responsibility with regard to his academic work. He indicated that he was now a senior, that he would be graduating, that he had not done enough work in college to justify his getting a degree, and that he was beginning to feel dissatisfied with himself. He was haunted by the idea that, although he felt mentally capable, he could not make himself "care enough." His peers regarded him as infallible, but he thought he was a "natural failure." He stated that if his professors knew how little he applied himself they would feel that he "should not be in school." The student felt that he had gotten pretty much of the "good life," and everything he wanted, but lately he had been chafing at his dependence upon others and now he wanted to earn his privileges. Having had indulgent parents, he never learned self-discipline.

The student looked upon his studies and his desires, or likes and dislikes, as being in conflict. He knew that he was not a C student and that he could do much better than he was doing at the moment. He concluded that, perhaps, he visited the college psychiatrist looking for another excuse to justify his doing poorly. During the conference he explored a number of possibilities; they included what his goals in life were, what he wanted from a college education, his guilt feelings over his parents' disappointment in his grades, his fear of studying and still not getting good grades, the exaggerations of his lack of self-confidence, and his satisfaction in telling others how little he studied and how little he liked college. After his conference, he recognized that he felt guilty over his relatively little motivation to do college work, and over his doing just the minimum of work to get by. The student was interested in examining some of his values and goals in life, and he experienced guilt, now that he was a senior, over his conduct during his preceding three years. The important thing is that he was interested in understanding himself better.

Although guilt is a legitimate cause for anxiety and depression, "guilt feelings," on the other hand, can be felt by the student merely because they provide security for him. Some students seem to enjoy expressing guilt feelings over conditions which normally should not be associated with such feelings. For example, a student with guilt feelings over an A— grade who says that he made "terrible mistakes" in the test (to account for the minus sign) is only boasting about himself in a subtle manner. Other students report feelings of guilt over mistakes and failures in order to pave the way for milder consequences. Our society is prone to be more sympathetic to those who admit feelings of guilt than to those who deny them. The student who arrives late for an examination and feels guilty about his tardiness may be treated with more understanding than if he did not express feelings of guilt. Still others, by focusing their attention on the annoyance that their guilt feelings give them, overlook the more important areas of life, and claim that these feelings render them helpless to do anything worthwhile in life. This argument is more convenient to the student than to admit failure in the academic and social area on account of personal shortcomings, as is shown in the next case.

A student visited the health service psychiatrist complaining of having guilt feelings which caused him to earn lower grades after he had changed his curriculum, despite his father's strong advice against the change, from Civil Engineering to the Humanities, in which he had greater interest. The father was described as a competent civil engineer who tended to dictate to his son the career he should choose. The student was not able to express his feelings of resentment toward his father, but had always been compliant.

It is evident that the student's "guilt feelings" were a justification for having to go against his father's wishes. He could then blame his father for compelling him to enter a field he did not want in the first place and at the same time attempt to appease and to draw sympathy and attention from him by doing poor work in the humanities. Guilt feelings also served as an excuse to cover up his hostility toward his father which he was not able to bring out in the open. After a few counseling interviews, he began to understand his relationship with his father, and the manner in which his guilt feelings served to legitimize his failure.

Although the ethical and moral standards of our society burden those who misbehave by creating guilt in them, the student should be aware that, at the same time, society offers means by which guilt can be eradicated and misconduct absolved. First, guilt can be considerably relieved if the student confesses his unacceptable act to a respectful and understanding person( counselor, minister). For example, a student who has violated his sexual code can repent for his act and gain relief from guilt. Secondly, he can overcome a sizable amount of guilt by employing behavior which makes amends for the deed that caused him to feel guilty. Thus, if guilt still annoys him, despite the fact that he has come to recognize his wrongdoing with deep regret, he can avoid the circumstances where it was easy for him to succumb to the morally unacceptable act. By doing this, he convinces himself that he *does* have control over his drives, and he, thus, reinforces a positive self-re-evaluation. As he proves to himself that he does not become the victim of his impulses, he will tend to eradicate the guilt resulting from his previous behavior. However, recreating the same circumstances in order to "test" himself is not always successful, for, should the student again fail, he becomes more guilt-ridden.

Thirdly, perhaps the most positive method of making one's guilt subside is not so much by thinking about it or by trying to forget it, but by engaging in an *activity* by which other members of his society may benefit, regardless whether his previous behavior had affected them or his own moral code. It is by his actions that he can make others aware of his positive contributions, and these contributions, in return restore him into the community as a respectable member.

Another common symptom which is similar to depression, but

usually in a milder degree is boredom. The student does not know how to occupy his time; yet, he cannot study. What appears to amuse others, to him seems dull. He cannot become interested in activities. He does not see much purpose in doing anything. Even the common forms of amusement seem "silly" to him. He sums up his whole attitude by saying: "I just have no interest in anything; I've tried to do many things but I get bored quickly and I give up. Everything seems empty. Whenever I think of doing anything, I can't imagine doing it the rest of my life." Such students find an occasional excitement, but they quickly fall back to their same pattern.

There is no student who will not, occasionally, feel this way during his college attendance. At certain times, it is perfectly normal for any intelligent and perceptive person to feel apathetic and indifferent towards life—as if he were apart from everything. Some students desire to be left alone for a while; this need does not necessarily violate the rules of emotional health. It is when these tendencies become prolonged and exaggerated to the point where he becomes inadequate in sustaining himself, and in coping efficiently with the tasks of college, that he is approaching failure. The majority of such students manage to find an interest in an area and to create meaningful goals for themselves if given enough time. The deeper reason for boredom is often unknown to the student (resentment, lack of identity, guilt, hostility, etc.).

While depression is considered as one of the most frequent emotional symptoms in college students, the opposite symptom, namely, *hypomania,* also occurs but in much fewer instances. Hypomania is characterized by great productiveness by a shifting in ideas and thoughts, by an increase in motor activity, and by a feeling of liveliness and physical well-being. The student exhibits a rise in spirits and ambition, he becomes involved in many activities, he argues easily, he takes issues quickly, and he is vigorous and enthusiastic. Such students are apt to be considered by their peers as being more active and alert than the average college student. It is when a student becomes annoying and overly extravagant, as when he incurs large debts, takes more courses than he can handle, loses sleep by participating in club activities, talks endlessly over trivia, and so forth, that his symptoms become less normal. At this stage, he can lose a meaningful perspective in his activities, and his overabundance of energy can incapacitate him. He seeks outlets for his energy which may not be of any use to him, or do not serve any purposeful goal.

Hypomania has been described as an unconscious attempt by the student to compensate for or to conceal his feelings of inferiority by foreseeing a bright future in which all his plans will work out for himself. He wishes to see all his ideas materialize. Since these aims obviously do not always become realized facts, the hypomanic student is most likely to shift into a state of depression in order to receive sympathy. In his depressive state he is considered "ill" and is, consequently, excused for his failures in achieving the goals he formulated while in the manic state. The hypomanic student feels basically inferior and inadequate, and he is afraid to face these feelings. Hence, he sets up superior goals to convince himself that he is not as weak as he feels. He avoids the issue by placing himself in a state of excitement and self-deceptive fearlessness. These changes in mood are not thought out consciously by the student, but are triggered into operation without his conscious awareness.

*     *     *     *

It should be clear to the student that many of the symptoms described, so far, in this chapter, are found in nearly every normal student and that, occasionally, they may become magnified. These magnified states the student should be able to recognize and to take the necessary steps. Concerning the mild symptoms, as he is able to understand their nature he can tolerate them easier, since, the ensuing maladjustment that occurs has, for the most part, a temporary quality. When the student begins to suffer from these symptoms, and when they are no longer of a transient nature, then these symptoms have developed into a more important condition which affects him more severely. It is with these magnified symptoms that the next chapter will deal.

There are a few general symptoms which, if present in the student for a long period of time in severe intensity, should warrant him to seek professional consultation. Constant worry over the possibility that something is going to happen, although in reality remote and unlikely; harboring a bleak outlook for the future when nothing warrants it; continuous feeling of suspicion and irritability; an excessive amount of inferiority feelings when there is no objective reason for the student to feel this way; intense moodiness and depression when things are going fairly well; becoming overwhelmed and overreacting to minor unfortunate events; severe reluctance to confide feelings and thoughts in anyone; inability to find purpose and content-ment; and frequent change of attitude about people from one extreme to the other—all are characteristics which can be alleviated if they are persistent in the student. Since there is a reason for every kind of behavior that exists, the student need not feel distress or wait until bothersome symptoms "go away," although they may subside after the student has suffered unnecessarily.

Anxiety and depression are predominantly psychological in nature. It is true that changes in personality must be accom-panied by changes in the brain and nervous system, but we do not know what is the exact relationship. There are special types of symptoms which are not only psychological in nature but are accompanied by real bodily complications, such as chronic fatigue, insomnia, skin diseases, high blood pressure, ulcers, heart and stomach trouble, and migraine headaches. These symptoms usually occur in those parts of the body that are controlled mainly by the autonomic nervous system. In other words, they take place in those organs of the body over which the person has no control. Thus, physical symptoms are aggra-vated by emotional states.

## The Meaning of Psychosomatic Symptoms

When the student is frequently bothered by certain thoughts, events, people, or if he constantly worries about himself, he cannot go on for long without developing some kind of symptom. Often, a threat to one's self, whether it is conscious or uncon-scious, real or imaginary, can be manifested through physical symptoms. A few of these symptoms may involve organs or systems in the body which either do not function well or are afflicted by pains. Loud and rapid heartbeats, cold sweats, indigestion, diarrhea, severe headaches—these are some of the typical symptoms. Usually, the physician will first examine the student to rule out the possibility of organic cause before he decides that the symptoms operate on a psychological basis. The digestive system is more easily affected by strain and is more sensitive to stress than the other organs of the human body. Nausea, feelings of being "tied up in knots inside," having "butterflies in the stomach," the loss of appetite during emotional stress, and constipation after encountering with a new environment are symptoms very familiar to the college student.

When bodily dysfunctions are caused by emotional problems, we have a category of symptoms called *psychosomatic.* A considerable number of students visit the college physician with bodily complaints only to discover that the results of the physical examination are negative. The students' complaints are certainly not imaginary. In such cases a thorough psychiatric examination reveals that the bodily complaints constitute a by-product of an adjustment problem. It is the general consensus that nearly all psychosomatic disorders are the outcome of tension and anxiety which flow into the body and create these symptoms. Hence, it would not be too practical to treat the physical symptoms and ignore the fundamental emotional problem behind the symptoms. Very often, students are able to associate their symptoms with some psychological problem that happens to be distressing them, and many experience relief from their symptoms. Others confuse psychosomatic symptoms with a real physical disease because of the similarity of symptoms. Following is a typical case.

A foreign student visited the health center physician requesting medication and treatment for his "heart trouble" which made it difficult for him to study and concentrate. The symptoms were described as pain in the chest, a rapid and loud heartbeat, an occasional pain in his left arm, and a slight amount of dizziness and periodical inability to breathe freely. When the physical examination, x-rays, and laboratory tests were all essentially negative, the physician assured the student that his physical symptoms, although symptomatically similar to heart disease, were due to an emotional condition. The student assumed that the diagnosis was a mistake and visited another physician who gave him a similar reply. Finally, in exasperation, the student carefully read books on heart disease in the medical library, and collected paragraphs that gave the exact description of his symptoms, and presented them to the health center physician he had originally consulted. After re-examination, the diagnosis remained negative of heart disease, and the student was eventually referred to the health center psychiatrist.

The student was at first reluctant to admit that he was aware of any emotional problem, and he could not see a connection between letting out his feelings and the symptoms he presented. He insisted upon receiving medication. Finally, the student became angry because his needs were not being met, and he began expressing negative feelings. He disclosed with tears and embarrassment that his father had literally forced him to come to this country and to earn a degree which would mean enhanced prestige for his family after he returned to his homeland. The student had never previously been able to let his father know that he had no interest, whatsoever, in studying abroad. As the student expressed his negative feelings in the permissive and accepting atmosphere of the psychiatrist's office during the subsequent interviews, the symptoms gradually lessened.

Every student who develops persistent physical symptoms should consult a physician. In many instances, these symptoms are predominantly psychosomatic in nature. Depending upon the annoyance they cause in the student he is at liberty to accept or reject the recommendation for psychotherapy or counseling. The student who is planning soon to leave college may not want to become involved with intensive treatment if he knows it will be interrupted suddenly. In most cases, psychotherapy is optional depending upon the student's desire to face the real source of his symptoms. Some students prefer to go on medication for a while and to treat the problem symptomatically, rather than to become involved with their emotions and thoughts. Although for milder and temporary symptoms psychotherapy is not usually mandatory, in cases with severe symptoms, as with the student mentioned above, psychotherapy or counseling is most likely to be recommended.

There is no one who has not felt, at some time during his lifetime, some mild psychosomatic manifestations. These symptoms nearly always accompany anxiety and tension. They are referred to as psychosomatic when the distress on an organ(s) becomes the primary focus of the symptoms, and anxiety is a secondary symptom. Prior to a difficult and competitive examination, for example, a great number of students sense a rapid heartbeat, frequent urination, dryness of the mouth, tremor and perspiration in the hands, and rapid breathing. After the examination, the symptoms usually disappear because the threat, fear or danger of failing, has disappeared. It is when these symptoms persist longer than normally expected that we have a true psychosomatic manifestation.

The student should accept the fact that the way he feels and thinks affects the organs of his body. Thus, when there are such symptoms present which cannot be explained on the basis of any definite physical disorder, the causes are likely to be found in the student's psychological structure. The symptoms, of course, are real (e.g., pains), but there is nothing wrong with the organs in which these symptoms appear. Often they are identical with the typical symptoms of well-known ailments. It would be wise for the student who has persistent physical symptoms to consult a physician and submit to any recommended special diagnostic studies and laboratory tests. If the results are negative, then the reasons for his physical symptoms are psychological.

Pressure creates anxiety and tensions, which can be channelled into special organs of the body. This process is not of the student's choice, nor can he predict the organ to be afflicted. For example, when a student is anxious, the secretion of gastric juices increases and prevents the healing of any existing lesions in the stomach. When such a person is given psychotherapy, his emotional or anxiety state tends to decrease and allows the organs of the body to function normally. As the student learns to cope with the causative problem, either by learning new techniques on better adjustment, or by understanding himself (his goals, attitudes, needs, expectations, etc.), he becomes able to go through the stress without much precipitating anxiety.

Thus, the physical symptoms either disappear or become weaker, and barely cause any further noticeable discomfort.

Since the human organism consists of a whole unit, one should expect that the physical condition of the person will affect his psychological state. Many students affected with mononucleosis become depressed, sluggish, and apathetic, an example of a physical disturbance creating temporary emotional symptoms. The student who complains of an emotional problem may, after a physical examination, discover that the psychological symptoms of which he originally complained, are the product of poor physical health (anemia, glandular disturbances, neurological disorder, etc.). It is not uncommon, however, for students to insist that all their emotional problems have a physical origin in order to avoid looking at themselves or to admit that there is "something mentally wrong."

The first step in the treatment of psychosomatic syndromes is for the student to realize that emotional factors are at play. Although this may relieve him of the fear of consequences from a physical ailment, he may take it as a weakness to admit that he has psychological problems. The psychiatrist or psychologist usually assures the student that guilt or shame about having a conflict is not peculiar only to him; otherwise, if this point is not made clear, the student will resist talking about himself. First, the therapist explores environmental factors to determine whether they can be linked to the onset of the symptoms. If an association can be made, the student is helped to understand the nature of these factors, and particularly why they affect his emotions. Second, with the assistance of the therapist the student can be guided to a clearer understanding of the fabric of his personality; also, the therapist can uncover and interpret to the student aspects of his personality of which he was unaware. The student eventually begins to learn new ways of responding to pressure connected with the symptoms. Surprisingly enough, symptoms tend to lessen with a few such sessions. Along with psychotherapy, medication, if needed, can also be administered by the psychiatrist.

*     *     *     *

College students are often burdened with symptoms of

anxiety, depression, or psychosomatic complaints, brought on by any number of reasons. In many cases where the symptoms described in this chapter appear in the student, he can handle them and the underlying problem by himself; sometimes he recruits the aid of friends, understanding parents, and members of the college faculty. The manner in which the student has handled these symptoms prior to attending college, and the experiences he has had with them in the past, will tend to make him react to them in a similar way later on. Others are able to learn to solve their personal problems that bring on these symptoms by applying the knowledge acquired through their studies. In a few instances, however, the student's symptoms do not diminish or even lighten despite his efforts to manipulate the conditions that aggravate these feelings. These symptoms require professional help, and the student is encouraged to seek it.

# 6

## MAJOR TYPES OF MALADJUSTMENT

M ENTAL HEALTH SERVICES in colleges and universities handle a great variety of emotional problems that cause students to seek assistance. The present chapter will describe the major types of problems that cause enough difficulty in students for them to obtain professional consultation. The purpose of this presentation is to familiarize the student with these problems, even though he may not be able to prevent them from occurring, just as he cannot avert physical ailments simply by learning about them. The objective of this section is not to oversell the idea that everyone needs treatment, or to make the student feel he is ill, but to enable him to understand when a problem is a *real* problem. Nondisabling problems are not considered real problems, in the true sense of the term, just as a mild form of the common cold does not make one essentially ill.

Many students seek help when they do not really need it, while others who never avail themselves of the existing mental health facilities in their college or community can benefit from such help. As the student learns to distinguish broad underlying concepts which explain these categories of maladjustment, he will know better what to do about them. He will understand that the thoughts and feelings characteristic of these maladjustments have been too intensified, but that, in small degrees, they are common in nearly every normal person. Also, he will know that the behavior resulting from these maladaptations constitutes a pattern which is pronounced and persistent, and that such behavior is universally found in almost every age level, although in very insignificant degrees.

## Neurosis

Perhaps the most common behavior pattern the student will meet is a neurosis, which appears when the person has conflicts within himself or with his environment. The neurotic is aware of his condition but does not know how to change it. The main element in the neuroses is *anxiety* which the student usually experiences consciously. The personality of a neurotic student is not grossly disorganized, and he does not show distortion of the environment to any noticeable degree. This person has not adjusted well to his environment because his energy is invested in the control of this anxiety. The methods for controlling anxiety are referred to as *mechanisms of adjustment* and have been already discussed. As previously stressed, everyone has a normal amount of anxiety that keeps him alert and aware of the problems of life. A real neurotic condition becomes apparent when the person feels overpowered either by excessive anxiety or by the exaggerated forms of certain mechanisms of defense.

When the mechanisms of defense become either too strong and rigid, or too weak and ineffective, the student's adjustment begins to fail. He feels uneasy and tense, and he experiences fears over activities and situations which, under normal circumstances, do not call for such worries. The greater the amount of anxiety present, the less the safeguard mechanisms are operating to control it. If the student becomes totally overwhelmed by anxiety, as indicated by inability to breathe freely, by crying spells, tenseness in the body, headaches, stomach "cramps," insomnia, fatigue, anorexia, etc., then, we have a syndrome known as *free floating anxiety* or *anxiety state*. These symptoms imply that the safeguard mechanisms are not working too well for the student. The aim of brief psychotherapy, which should properly follow the administration of drugs, is to enable the student to resolve the cause of his anxiety and to strengthen his psychological defenses. Sometimes medication may be necessary to make the anxiety tolerable until effective psychotherapy can be instituted. Below is a typical case.

A seventeen-year-old male freshman consulted a physician at the college dispensary, complaining of insomnia, and fatigue. He had frequent crying spells and had a dreadful fear that something catastrophic was going to happen to him in the future. There was a severe tremor in his hands, and he felt that his heart was beating loudly and rapidly. He complained of inability to concentrate and pursue a goal without being easily distracted by his thoughts about his health. He told of having periodic pains in the chest and the stomach, and of feeling "just sick all over." The physical examination was essentially negative. It was disclosed that his parents and relatives had formed a fund so that he could attend college and become a physician, but the student could not possibly visualize himself ever becoming a physician; he had no ambition to go to college. He had an acute type of anxiety which subsided in a few days with medication. He decided to leave college for at least one year, and to return if he felt ready for a career in medicine or some other field.

Neurosis becomes known by the crippling symptoms it forms. Some of these symptoms are so mild that a truly neurotic pattern is not easily established. A real case of neurosis constitutes anxiety in the student which is disproportionate to the situation. For instance, if the student becomes constantly tense when he has to eat at the same table with other students, if he continually has dreadful fears when he is about to leave home to return to college, or if he exhibits an intense feeling of apprehension when left alone in the street, he is likely to be manifesting neurotic symptoms. Also, unreasonable and repetitious actions, such as sterilizing everything he touches, taking six baths a day, or requiring several hours to write a one-page letter, and severe and unjustifiable fears as when crossing a bridge, or being in a small group of people, can also indicate neurotic tendencies. Of course, any normal person occasionally exhibits these same feelings; they take on a neurotic quality only when they persist and are severe.

There are six major types of neuroses, which are mainly aggravations of normal feelings and thoughts. Severe anxiety and depression that deprive the student of his capacity to function are two of the most frequent neurotic symptoms in students. It is the intensity and keenness of these symptoms and their longer duration when compared with transient manifestations of anxiety or depressive symptoms that give them their neurotic characteristics. The remaining symptoms of neurotic patterns are the exaggerated types of the four last defense mechanisms discussed in Chapter 4—phobia, obsession-compulsion, conversion, and dissociation. A few explanatory comments on the most common of these, phobia and obsession-compulsion, will follow.

Every normal student can find minor compulsions and phobias within himself. Indeed, very few persons are not afraid of some kind of animal (mice, snakes), or do not unnecessarily overdo some act (scrupulosity, cleanliness, punctuality). But if we take an hypothetical case of a person who develops a severe panic whenever he enters any type of moving vehicle, can never walk in the street unless accompanied by someone, or must wash his hands immediately after he touches objects that were handled previously by someone else, he becomes grossly incapacitated, and others become alarmed over his behavior. Although he knows his behavior is irrational and inappropriate, he cannot control it nor can he forget his fears, in fact, the more he tries to "forget" his compulsions and fears, the more uncomfortable he becomes. Except for minor symptoms which are not annoying to the subject, such severe conditions are not very common among college students. However, the prognosis is fairly good even in the severe cases which require treatment, usually lasting over extended periods of time.

Every student has a small amount of neurosis of which he is not fully aware. It is barely noticeable to others, and it seldom annoys him. The symptoms can become more obvious when he is under stress, such as becoming tense before exams (test-anxiety). The symptoms ordinarily disappear as soon as the stress is over. Under these circumstances, the student obviously is not a neurotic, unless the symptoms are prolonged and damaging to his interpersonal conduct and personal well-being. Students with neurotic patterns usually respond well to psychotherapy; some recover even without treatment. A case of true neurosis is one in which anxiety is not controlled adequately by the mechanisms of defense, and the student begins to feel his anxiety. Or, neurosis may be due to his safeguard mechanisms becoming too strong and rigid.

It must be pointed out that since everyone has anxiety and

neurotic predispositions which can bring on a neurosis when these symptoms become exaggerated, the prevalence of neurosis is much greater than is psychosis. In fact, neurotic traits are so common in our time that many people no longer consider them unusual, as long as they do not become outstandingly obnoxious. Thus, with respect to the neurosis of students the outlook is very favorable. In certain instances drugs are used to minimize the symptoms and to facilitate his progress with psychotherapy, the aim of which is to encourage the student to look at his real problem, and to motivate him to deal with it more effectively. Those students who have more intense neurotic symptoms than others can still manage to be productive in their work and feel very little annoyance from these symptoms.

## Psychosis

Psychosis, on the other hand, is a mental illness. The psychotic patient has lost contact with the world; his behavior in response to it is not consistent with those with whom he lives. His responses are meaningful to him, but appear bizarre and illogical to his observers. There is a tendency for his intellectual processes to deteriorate and for his emotions to become inconsistent with his thoughts. To him the world is seen *subjectively* and evaluated without consideration for external reality. His stream of thinking becomes unpredictable, inconsistent, and tangential. He lacks insight and awareness into his condition, and cannot make the distinction between his phantasies and the real world. The psychotic does not know he is ill, and at times he may not be oriented in time and place. Finally, the psychotic may hear and see things that are not there. The legal term for psychosis is *insanity*. There are several types of psychosis and each has its distinct characteristics. However, this book will not discuss the subclasses of psychosis, but will limit itself to the general idea of psychosis only.

Psychosis is one of the less-common emotional disturbances among college students. Although it is the most severe of all the emotional problems, some students with this illness manage to complete their education—even with excellent grades! Most characteristic of the college student with psychosis is his general disorientation, bizarreness, and his unusual and eccentric thoughts and actions. He does not know what he should do, and he aims at utterly high and unrealistic goals. He may require many hours for preparation of material that other students accomplish in much less time. He can appear intense and methodical, but he absorbs very little because only a meager amount of what he reads registers in his mind. His thinking goes off easily on a tangent, and he often talks about a subject completely different from the one he first started. The psychotic student often goes into minute details in his speaking and tends to incorporate irrelevant material into what he originally wanted to say. Much of his thinking and verbalizations is illogical or incomprehensible, and they may persevere as he repeats the same words or phrases. His ability to comprehend general ideas is impaired because he contaminates events or facts and he arrives at the wrong conclusion. Although he may appear articulate, he can easily miss the main point in a topic. His mind may suddenly begin to wander, and his ability for sustained attention is impaired.

His relationships with other students are often superficial and tenuous. He approaches people not so much out of genuine friendship but mostly to gain something from them—to derive some benefit by seeking reassurances, and to satisfy his needs of dependency. The psychotic student has difficulty finding meaning in activities which most people enjoy and appreciate. If he is failing, he may have fantastically unrealistic hopes that he will succeed. The main characteristic of this type of student is that he is not aware of the reality around him, and his self-appraisal is distorted. The emotions, feelings, and desires which are the basis of and regulate his thoughts and conduct are distorted and out of order.

Characteristic of the few students who develop psychosis in college is that they lived a comparatively normal childhood, and their psychotic illness at college is of an acute nature and lasts a short period. He is not withdrawn and bizarre to the same degree as the typical psychotic person in a mental hospital and his chances of recovery are very good. His "breakdown" is usually the result of a specific stress situation, e.g., rejection, not having found someone to whom he can communicate his feelings, inability to accept and to resign himself to his low self-esteem, and inadequate preparation to take on roles he desires to play. He does not feel competent enough to manipulate his environment, and minor problems are exaggerated and seem insurmountable. Finally, the psychotic student is very dependent upon others, he has little respect for himself, and he is afraid of becoming completely isolated from people. The following case exhibits a clear, psychotic episode.

A male student was referred to a college psychiatrist because he was overtalkative, overactive, was suspicious that his teachers would not let him graduate, and was belligerent toward his fraternity brothers. His roommates gave a history of bizarre behavior, disordered thinking, reversal of his sleep pattern, and inability to function as a student. In the classroom the student was in a constant state of restlessness, and was causing disturbance with his gibberish. He would move his arms around in the air, slam his books down repeatedly, and move his feet around conspicuously. He placed his glasses upside down and rolled his head around in a distracting fashion. Again and again he would snap his fingers loudly and wave his hands wildly about. He quarreled with basic and most obvious statistical facts, his voice often rising higher and higher until the instructor feared he was becoming hysterical and interrupted him. Usually, what he had to say bore little relevance to the topic under discussion. He tended to exhibit ideas of reference, i.e., believing that many people were speaking about him and that they were definitely against him. He also rationalized his behavior, insofar as whatever happened was really not his fault but the result of some emotional state brought about by outside forces.

The psychiatrist could not elicit any meaningful material from him. The student insisted that although he was "emotional," this was his usual mood and could not understand why so many people were so concerned about him. He explained further that many persons had advised him to "get help" after they became acquainted with him. He related further that whenever he visited a psychiatrist in the past, he was asked why he was there and what was the problem. Since the student was unable to state clearly any specific problem, he, by himself, had come to the conclusion that there was nothing wrong with him. He felt that the fact that others had suggested he see a psychiatrist, was a good enough reason for him to be suspicious, and he guarded against any advice which hinted that he was in need of treatment for an emotional problem.

At first, the student refused to enter the psychiatrist's office; however, he did so after much persuasion and firmness. He talked continuously, and he occasionally trembled with rage at remarks made concerning his lack of judgment and insight into his mental status. His stream of thought was disjointed and accelerated. His mental associations were grossly loosened, and his speech was incoherent and irrelevant. Attempts to evaluate abstracting and calculating ability and his orientation were answered with rage and indignation. He described someone reading his mind and spoke at length about various philosophers and religions, and he expressed ideas of world destruction. He asserted that he was able to tell the contents of a letter before he opened it, and that he could somehow predict the personality of the nurses, the doctor, and the attendants by thinking about the letters of the first and last name and by the sound of these letters. The student refused to give information about himself because he felt that the use of the past tense was a contradiction of his existentialist philosophy. He admitted that he had not eaten properly because water and air were sufficient to maintain life.

The student in this case required intensive psychiatric treatment in a psychiatric hospital. Since this was an acute type of psychosis, the prognosis was very favorable. Also, his not having any previous history of emotional difficulty, and his age, both indicated a rapid recovery. Upon leaving the hospital, the student was placed under the care of a private psychiatrist, for a few months, who treated him with medication and psychotherapy. Meanwhile, the student worked during this time. He returned to college in excellent remission. When he was seen again by the college psychiatrist for the routine psychiatric clearance, he was hesitant and embarrassed to discuss his past behavior because "it all seems so silly now." Although he was able to recall nearly all the instances of his illness, he was ashamed to talk about them again.

What made this student develop a psychotic illness? This is not an easy question to answer, because there are many factors involved and many of them are not known until the student has undergone a fairly long term of treatment. Of course, his excessive emotionality may play a role, to some extent, in his becoming ill. But many people who are considered to be "emotional" may live perfectly normal lives and never develop a psychosis or anything as severe as this student exhibited. Hence, there must be something else besides the predominant characteristics of one's personality. A person may have certain predispositions in his personality which can be more or less innate. But nothing may happen throughout the whole course of his lifetime, until something in the environment which is stressful and unpleasant to him *precipitates* psychotic behavior. It is not the innate tendency alone, nor the unpleasant event in the environment by itself that causes mental illness, but *both* are responsible and are taken into consideration when the person's illness is evaluated.

In the case of our student, several factors in his family may have been responsible for his illness, in addition to his being "emotional." (1) He was close to and dependent upon his mother who began suffering from an incurable disease at about the time when the student's emotionality was noted to have increased. By becoming hyperactive on subjects that were not directly related to his real problem, he managed to conceal his own inner turmoil over the possible loss of his mother. (2) He had been very close to a sister who had exhibited antisocial and delinquent behavior, much to the embarrassment of the family; at the time his symptoms began to manifest themselves, she wanted to marry a divorcee with three children, and his family was against such a venture. (3) The student was doing poorly in school and he was very perturbed that his father, who highly valued education and was willing to pay for it, would outwardly reject him. By developing an "illness" that required treatment, he found a reasonable excuse for having failed in college. Obviously, students rarely become psychotic because of academic failure alone. In nearly all cases there must be other factors present which, along *with* the academic failure, precipitate the illness.

In the case of psychosis, hospitalization is required in most instances because the student's personality is so disorganized that others become alarmed, and he can be a menace to them and to himself. To other students he often appears odd and irrational. These peculiarities alone, of course, do not always suggest the presence of psychosis. Only professional persons who are experts in the diagnosis of mental illness should be consulted if psychosis is suspected, and they can undertake the proper treatment procedure if psychosis is established. Milder cases of psychosis can be treated with drugs on an outpatient basis at the dispensary or psychiatric services of the college. Small educational institutions without these facilities usually refer the student to medical or psychiatric services in the community. The idea is that even with some psychotic symptoms the student can still function as a student, as long as he is under some kind of treatment and the environment is not too demanding of him.

There are several methods of handling a psychosis. Severe cases always require medical intervention. The more acute the onset, the better will be the prognosis. Medication is often dispensed along with other forms of therapy. Most students recover and are able to return to college and continue their education. If psychosis was present from childhood, then the outlook is not so optimistic. Drugs are used for the psychotic student more often than with other psychiatric disorders. Group therapy has also been found to be effective in fostering independency and social adaptation in the psychotic student. The aim of psychotherapy is to give the student emotional support and to orient him in improving his testing of reality. He is encouraged to associate with other healthy students, and to avoid isolation as much as possible.

The neuroses and psychoses occurring in college students are nearly always of a functional nature. They constitute manifestations originating from an inadequate adjustment and from severe conflicts, rather than from any known physical changes in the nervous system. Some psychoses, however, can have an organic origin; these are more common among older people because of the natural impairment and deterioration of their nervous system. On rare occasions, students can manifest an organic psychosis, i.e., psychotic symptoms that have an organic basis. Lesions and diseases of the brain tissue due to injury and inflammation, drugs that affect the nervous system, tumors, excessive alcohol for a prolonged period—all these factors can make the student behave in a psychotic manner. As the physical causes are removed, the psychotic symptoms usually disappear. Psychosis from organic factors is usually treated with medication and sometimes with surgery.

## Personality Disorders

Mental health teams in colleges and universities are already familiar with a special variety of patterns of behavior which is not so much dependent upon unconscious conflicts and needs, but which reflects a personality development that has been irregular and interrupted by family, social and personal conflicts. These traits and patterns of behavior are generally referred to as *personality disorders.* Generally, personality disorders constitute traits and patterns that are found in the student's personality, as they are reflected from his behavior. In these disorders, the student does not experience any great amount of psychological distress, and he is usually less anxious. If, occasionally, he experiences emotional symptoms (anxiety, depression), they are generally secondary to the existing personality disorder. The basic factor in these disorders is that the student continues to exhibit traits and patterns of behavior which he did not outgrow during the process of development from childhood, and that he responds to stress in less mature ways. These disorders can be better understood as primarily *a way of behaving,* rather than as an emotional or mental symptom which involves disabling feelings and thoughts.

There is a large variety of personality disorders, and most persons normally have traces of some of these disorders in a very mild degree. While constitutional factors may play a role in the development of personality disorders, more important are the student's learning experiences that occurred during his development. Sometimes these disorders can be an asset for the student, depending on the type of occupation that he expects to adopt. For example, in occupations demanding leadership, a mild form of refined social aggressiveness is desirable; but compliant and passive individuals will, most likely, do well in those situations where one is most effective when he is a follower. For the most part, students with personality disorders have little difficulty with social effectiveness and adaptation to college, unless, of course, the disorder is severe.

Most students who seek help for a personal problem tend to exhibit personality disorders in various degrees, rather than the other types of maladjustment. Some, having originated from childhood, are of long duration, while others appear during the adolescent development. As with neurosis, every student has mild characteristics of some form of personality disorder which may not be readily perceptible unless one knows the student well. In fact, these traits are so common that the student has to show a marked deviation before he can consider himself as having a real personality disorder. Being impulsive and demanding when frustrated, exhibiting a history of social inadequacy, manifesting extreme dependency in making decisions, resorting to alcohol and drugs when faced with strain, and having conflicts with the law are common symptoms typical of personality disorders. Nearly every student has, more or less, acted mildly in these ways in one form or another.

Students with personality disorders may experience difficulty with the control of their emotions when they become frustrated; they may be either too dependent or too independent; and, they may have difficulty relating to society and authority. As with neurosis and psychosis, personality disorders create difficulty for the student when they become disproportionately strong, as compared to what is usually found in the average person. The next section of this chapter will describe some of the most typical classes of behavior disorders found among college students.

## Passive-aggressive Behavior

Passive-aggressive behavior is characteristic of those persons who are basically dependent, and who lack self-trust and self-reliance. When they meet with personal difficulties and normal stress situations, they tend to react to them in either of two typical ways: (1) By refusing to do what is normally expected of them; by remaining inactive and indecisive; and by seeking others for support, decisions, and guidance. (2) By displaying hostility and opposition toward others; by irritability and stubbornness; and by exhibiting active-destructive behavior. Children often display this type of behavior; adolescents and young adults are expected to have outgrown them. However, normal adults do, occasionally, exhibit mild forms of passive-aggressive behavior which has no real social or personal consequences. Below is a typical example of passive-aggressive behavior.

An eighteen-year-old male student identified his problem primarily as being challenged by anything he was asked to do. Consequently, he was easily involved in one difficulty or another. The student thought of himself as having been an independent individual for most of his life; furthermore, he was not interested in college, but was there to please his parents. He had no idea in what he should prepare himself for the future. He stated that until recently he felt confident in acting out his negativistic behavior, but that now he was beginning to feel less confident, and he wanted to discuss his behavior with someone. He felt that the fact that his parents had refused to buy him a car meant that he was not wanted at home. The previous summer he had resigned from his job because he had a premonition, rising from the fact that he had not done thoroughly what he had been hired to do, that eventually he would be fired. He enjoyed contradicting his parents, and, although he carried out his promises, he was deliberately slow in executing them, knowing that in this manner he irritated his parents. Whenever his parents told him to do something around the house, he flatly refused; he worked in the house only if it was his own idea, and not his parents'.

In the evening, he stayed up late studying leisurely in order to prevent fatigue from setting in, with the consequences that in the morning he overslept and missed his classes and quizzes which necessitated special arrangements with his instructors to make up these exams. Although he claimed to be "independent" of his parents, he missed them when he was away at college, where he could not provoke them. However, occasionally, he discontinued writing to them and ignored their letters until they became worried; then, he would send them an apologetic telegram saying he was fine. Another "kick" he enjoyed doing was to go out of his way in pleading to arrange a date, only to cancel it the same day saying that he had to be "out of town" for "unexpected important business." He explained that the purpose of this behavior was to prove to himself that he can be independent of others.

Many students often behave in a similar way but not to the same degree. We notice, in the above case, how the student makes demands upon his parents, manipulates his instructors, and punishes those he feels are oppressing him. It is noticeable that he feels inferior to females, and that he manages to disappoint them, which suggests that he himself is a deeply disappointed person. He strives to appear independent, although basically he is very dependent. After the student was seen in therapy, he was able to realize that although his need for independence is a very healthy one, it was not necessary for him to obstruct people and to appear aggressive. The real meaning of independence began to develop in him: it emphasized the attainment of status on one's own merit and efforts, without having to put others under his control. It became apparent to him that independence grows from within as the student feels he is achieving within his own abilities and interests, rather than by restraining and dominating others. Passive-aggressive behavior cannot be eradicated entirely, but it can be reduced to the point where the student can function with less interpersonal friction.

Demonstrating stubbornness when helpful and realistic advice is offered, the showing of academic inefficiency when the student is actually superior, pouting or avoiding conversation on dates by the partner who feels he has been "hurt" by the other, the postponing of decisions where others are going to be affected (graduation, marriage), the "forgetting" of important plans and deadlines thereby upsetting the course of events, the eluding and resisting of giving personal information in situations where it is required (employment, medical), the delaying of actions that must be done immediately, making others wait but being impatient when having to wait for others—all are examples of passive-aggressive behavior. Normally, of course, everyone, at times, behaves in this manner. If this type of behavior is too persistent, it implies that the student cannot tolerate his passiveness and inferiority; but instead of outgrowing them in a healthy way by achieving and excelling in his major interests and talents, he acquires a false sense of superiority over others as he controls them by exhibiting his aggression via the passive maneuverings described above. He can go only so far, and before long he finds himself defeated by his own aggressiveness in the college milieu.

Passive-aggressive behavior, which is often shown in rebelliousness against the authority of parents and other parent-like figures, can be detected by the way the student behaves in college. He can embarrass his parents by acting antisocially "for fun" (rowdiness, drinking, pranks), and by exhibiting behavior that is unbecoming to a college student. His excuse may be that he was influenced by his peers. Another way to "get even" with parents and other authority symbols is to fail academically, which is not done deliberately but by developing psychological symptoms which cannot sustain the student in college. Often, the parents of these students have status and power in the community, and the student can feel that he has been compelled to excel; thus, he "fights back" by passive-aggressive patterns of behavior. Interestingly enough, some of these students who fail after having shamed their parents experience little guilt, and later return spontaneously to college to become excellent students, as if now the battle against parents has ended.

It must be remembered that adjustment to any type of situation in which human interaction takes place implies a harmony between the needs of an individual and those with whom he interacts. The student whose responsibility has been taken away from him, and who was given more than he really needed, will encounter various degrees of difficulty in college where the competitive spirit is present. When the student's needs are not being met, as they were when he was a child, he may try to manipulate instructors for special favors, or he may make extra demands on those he is dependent upon by placing them into his service. Here we have the picture of the chronic com-
work for it. He may blame his failure upon apparent faults in
plainer who desires to obtain a degree but is not willing to

the college system, or he may blame those who do not wish to succumb to his whims. In childhood, he may have been allowed to dominate through passive-aggressive behavior; in college, he cannot continue to do so without personal friction.

Frustration and conflict, also, can precipitate passive-aggressive behavior and negativism. It must be understood that everyone has some negativism which he has not fully outgrown from childhood. As an adult however, he expresses it in ways that are accepted by society, such as, being occasionally disciplined to cooperate in voluntary projects, or not accepting beneficial advice from colleagues. The maladaptive form of negativism is expressed through unnecessary boldness, disobedience, and antagonism toward persons who are interested in his welfare. These actions, of course, invite defiance and help the student to gain attention. He often exhibits such behavior in order to frustrate others for no apparent reason, and he may not be too concerned with the consequences of his behavior. Such a student often gains a false sense of mastery over his environment, and conceals his feelings of inferiority which he does not want to admit to himself.

Feeling inferior as a student and unworthy as a person can be manifested not only through passive-aggressive behavior, but also by a hostile attitude and by being actively destructive and openly resentful. Obviously, such behavior can lead to actions that are generally opposed by the standards of conduct in our society. The democratic, open society in which we live condones a reasonable amount of aggression as long as others do not suffer from it. With respect to college students, hostility and aggression most frequently originate from a deep feeling of resentment, as a reaction against punitive parental authority which is carried over to other such parent-like figures as educators, clergy, and even competitive peers. For others they may be due to a long-standing self-dissatisfaction.

Behind aggressive behavior there is frequently some type of frustration. As the child is disciplined to conform to parental and social expectancies, he begins to associate any kind of control from the outside as a frustrating experience. As a student in college, he frequently cannot manage frustrations and a variety of interpersonal annoyances without becoming resentful and anxious. Since any controls from the environment will increase his anxiety, control from within becomes the major objective of psychotherapy for him. To some extent, everyone becomes aggressive at times in ways that are socially condoned, such as excelling at sports and participating in debating clubs. These outlets are compatible with social expectations and are not injurious to one's emotional health.

## Passive-dependent Behavior

The student who has been overly pampered and overprotected by parents tends to develop into a dependent person. Because he was given more than he needed, or had responsibility taken away from him, he expects everyone in college to continue caring for his needs. By his passivity, he tyrannizes others because, eventually, they will have to work and contribute more than he. He controls others through his dependency. Every person is basically dependent to some degree; this is one reason why people marry. Even society functions on the interdependency of its members. If the student seeks others solely to satisfy his own dependency alone, rather than to participate and share with them, then he will have more difficulty in his adaptation to college than will the less dependent student. Dependent students drift into careers which do not stress personal initiative, and socially they are followers rather than leaders.

The passive-dependent student constantly needs support and assurance in making decisions. He tends to cling to others in order to overcome his helplessness. Such a student often has difficulty *giving*, in the broad sense of the word. He is more comfortable when others perform most of the work around him, and sometimes he expects others to give more and to expect less from him. He often lacks a clear concept of what he should do, and he constantly seeks advice for trivial tasks; he may even exaggerate his felt inabilities so that others can give him special attention and sympathize with him. He becomes easily timid when others are aggressive toward him, although physically he may *appear* aggressive. In many instances, satisfying solutions for the problems of dependency can be worked out better in real life situations than in private talks with a psychotherapist. Following is a good example of a demanding, dependent student.

A female student complained of feeling confused and of being unable to find any enjoyment in life. She was critical toward other members of her sorority and of her boyfriend because they all reacted toward her in an inane and immature way; she accused them of being "dumb" and "silly." She stated further that she had been "giving and not getting," and that she tended to "eat and eat" when she felt lonely and when people were indifferent toward her. She always had a deep fear of loneliness and felt emotionally "empty." She considered herself as being able to make the right decisions; she liked to tell others what to do, but she could not make friends easily. She belittled other people, and in doing so she saw them as being emotionally deprived persons—which is the same way she felt about herself but was afraid to face these feelings. This student had broken up with several boys in a relatively short time. Nearly all of her most vivid recollections from the past were scenes involving food and eating.

Although the student found her boyfriend distasteful, because of her strong dependency she could not afford to give him up. She said, "He's always around when I need someone to go out with; he never fails me; I like to know he's there; I always want to lean on someone who's understanding and who can love me." She said that he had complained about her attitude toward him. The student stated further that she could not make friends because "they can't give me what I want; I want someone who is stimulating and interesting and that I can respect. It's funny though, that when I meet someone I like, I just get shy and can't say anything to him." The student desired to be given things and to be provided with emotional supplies; but she simultaneously reacted to people with an aloofness and an air of independence, as if she was trying to hide her anger or her hurt feelings for having been ignored by them.

A few sessions with the psychologist helped the above student understand that security and a sense of belonging comes from thinking of others first. She also began to see that she could be of value and meaning to others when they received some benefit and gain that came from her own initiative. The student was confronted with the fact that the receiving of attention and support necessitates reciprocation; that if she wanted to be genuinely satisfied she would have to invest in other people by way of gratifying *their* needs. She progressively realized that everyone is basically dependent, but that most people consider the same need in others. Once this fact was emotionally felt in her, she was able to experience more feeling *for* people, and to make spontaneous thrusts that satisfied both her own and other people's emotional needs. She was also encouraged to apply these new insights to real-life situations, with some success. As she was helped to feel equal and less dependent on others, she became a more significant participant.

The student described above presents the picture of a clinging girl who relies strongly on other people for support, and who constantly needs to reassure herself that someone is interested in her. Her enjoyment in eating is symbolic of the need to be nurtured and taken care of, as the young child finds pleasure and security when his wants are satisfied. It is commonly observed that other students notice her dependency and avoid her. Since the dependent student must *gradually* learn to achieve his independence, it is not enough for him merely to know *why* he became dependent. Many students are unaware of their extreme dependency; they are in a comfortable position which is difficult to eliminate, unless they are shown and made to feel that the advantages of being more independent are greater. The excessively dependent student will achieve greater independence if he begins to feel that his dependency is interfering with his growth and achievement. In the previous case, the student was unable to form effective interpersonal relationships. Not only she but those with whom she interacted were dissatisfied and felt abused by her. In therapy, emotional independence is attained by gradually withdrawing the supplies which prolong the student's dependency, by encouragement, and by reinforcing the positive side of independent living.

Another dependency characteristic shows up in those who tend to criticize and make demands on others for not showing concern for other people; they sense a lack of such feelings in themselves, and for their own protection they attribute this lack to others. Dependency can also become manifested in emotional attachments to the opposite sex. Some students gratify their dependency by becoming emotionally attached to a relatively independent student of the opposite sex. Yet, this combination is fairly normal as long as both are satisfied with such a relationship.

The college can create dependency in the student when he feels he is being burdened with standards that make little sense to him. He wants to feel that he is accomplishing something on his own initiative. The student wants to feel needed, and appreciated for what he has to offer. When working and living with successful adults whom he respects and admires, he often envies their position and he wants to be like them. However, he has not yet developed their techniques and wisdom to think and act as they do, as he has not reached full emotional development. In order to compensate for his own feelings of awkwardness and inferior status, he is prone to look upon adults as "old-fashioned." The student wants to feel that his accomplishments have come about through his own decisions and efforts, and not because some adult thought he should carry them out. Success in college depends largely on the degree of the student's ability to carry out tasks compatible with his interests, with a minimum of dependency on others.

## Sociopathic Behavior

This category of personality disorders refers to those persons who are constantly having difficulties with *society* or the *law*, and who have considerable difficulty learning from their experiences. Such persons usually lack insight and blame other persons and society for their own difficulties; as a result, they do not have guilt feelings for their behavior. In other words, they lack a strong conscience and feel little remorse as they hurt other peoples' feelings. Even if they do express emotions and compassion, such expressions are apt to be not genuine but rather superficial in order to impress others and to gain their favor. The relation of the person with sociopathic traits to other people is usually exploitive since he interprets life as centering around him. He may also be dangerous because, when superficially viewed, he appears normal.

Students who exhibit such behavior are in conflict with the regulations of society, the moral codes of their environment, and authority. These students are defiant toward college authorities, they may be more frequently apprehended by the police for misdemeanors, they identify with special student groups which are hostile toward intellectual achievement, and they think it is clever to defraud exams and to violate college regulations. Such a student typifies the antisocial personality; he often, in a glib manner, attempts to manipulate college authorities whenever he gets into difficulty, and he looks upon himself as being the victim of college rules. He rationalizes his antisocial behavior by claiming that the college violates his individuality and that it is out to get him. Hence, he is now justified to "fight back at them." His aggressiveness can be disguised under the pretense of trying to reform the college and society.

The psychopath disregards the reactions of others toward him, and he finds it difficult to cooperate. He ignores the consequences his actions will have upon himself and society, and he has difficulty evaluating his behavior from another person's viewpoint. The psychopath cannot predict what others will do, and he is not sensitive to the reactions of others toward his unsocial behavior. Essentially, he does not experience conflict *within* himself, but rather his social behavior is in opposition to the accepted ways of behaving of the society in which he lives. Although psychopathic behavior is not very typical of the college student there are occasional incidents, as in the case below.

> An eighteen-year-old male student was referred for evalua-
> tion to the health service by one of the deans. He had been
> apprehended for stealing hubcaps and for trying to cash a
> check without having a bank account. His social history re-
> vealed that at the age of seven he had taken money from his
> father's clothes. The boy was sent home by the manager of the
> corner drugstore, who became suspicious when he saw him
> carrying the large amount of money. In spite of his constant

promises to reform, his stealing was repetitive. When he began driving, he was caught several times going through red lights, but he was usually able to manipulate the judge by convincing him that he was innocent. In school he had always been considered a "phoney" because he usually did not carry out his promises. His friends envied him because he was capable of finding plausible excuses for his behavior.

Whether or not this type of student will eventually change his behavior simply because college regulations curtail such behavior is difficult to answer. Of course, some students of this type mature with time, but such a change is not likely to happen. Since the student described in the previous case is mentally capable and responsible for his actions, he was faced with the consequences of his antisocial behavior, and was placed on conduct probation. In order to effect some change in the student's behavior, his continued enrollment in college was contingent upon receiving psychotherapy. Meanwhile, the student was advised that should the same behavior repeat itself, his emotional problems would not be accepted as an excuse, even though he was receiving treatment. In most colleges and universities, misconduct is handled first administratively, and treatment usually follows as a secondary recommendation.

Obviously, very few students display such behavior patterns, but the few that are found in college can cause considerable difficulty. Hence, college is not always the best place for these students. Some are lured into the university because they can hide behind academic activities, and they seem to find some form of refuge in the college environment until their behavior becomes noticeable. Those who exhibit this pattern in a severe manner are unable to survive in college and, eventually, either drop out or are asked to leave for disciplinary reasons. Since it requires longer time to rehabilitate the student with long-standing socio-pathic traits, many colleges and universities are not able to offer him the kind of psychological treatment that would be most beneficial to him.

If the pattern is relatively mild, however, he can benefit from psychotherapy provided that he is motivated to change. Paradoxically, his intellectual potential is often above average, but he is reluctant to undergo therapy in order to make his behavior more socially acceptable because he considers any form of treatment as a "gimmick" to make him conform. With severe cases, therapy will require more than a few weeks or months, which is not too practical for the student who leaves at the end of the quarter or semester. In such a case, college health authorities would normally recommend the student to other mental health agencies where he can undergo prolonged therapy. The treatment for those with sociopathic traits focuses on the redefinition of the character of society, and on the needs and attitudes of the student's own personality which create his unsocialized behavior. Sociopathic traits can lead the student into any number of delinquent acts and have caused great concern among mental health researchers.

## Delinquent Behavior

Delinquency is a behavioral phenomenon that usually occurs during the adolescent and early adulthood years. During the last decades there has been a greater awareness of the problem of delinquency. Statistics show that the delinquency rate has increased during the past few years. Professional workers in the field of mental health stress that delinquency is only a symptom of an underlying psychological problem. As a rule, by changing a person's delinquent behavior in making it more acceptable to social standards, the real causes of his behavior are not removed. There are numerous causes for delinquency, and each specialist in the field of mental health tries to attack the problem from a different aspect. It is generally believed that bad behavior is due to unfavorable environmental conditions, and that delinquents can learn good behavior. However, the physical environment is not the sole factor, for there are many persons who live in an unfavorable situation and do not become delinquents.

Delinquency has an important meaning in our culture, since inferiority, dependency and anything associated with weakness can easily be concealed by antisocial behavior. Such behavior is, unfortunately, easily labeled as being "musculine," "courageous" and "strong." Some students who felt they were unjustly punished by their parents cannot become hostile to their own parents, possibly from fear that they might be further rejected but find it easier to rebel against authority figures such as the professor, employer, and other authorities. Those who are unhappy with their environment may seek to conceal their discontent by seeking thrills and excitement at society's expense. Others who feel unaccepted by their social or academic circles will show a tendency to seek out and identify with a group that will accept them. Such a group can be the delinquent gang. Finally, those who feel guilty for other reasons may unconsciously seek punishment in order to eliminate the guilt feelings.

Delinquents are usually those persons who feel rejected by their parents, and come from families with strong marital disharmony living in a deteriorated area. Other factors are rebellion against authority, and feelings of frustration and of personal inferiority in relation to their peers. It is the person who feels he is a misfit or out of place in a social group who acts antagonistically, in order to show he is not a weakling and to convince himself of his capability of getting the attention of others. Punishment and other corrective means have not been very effective, since the delinquent is fighting society and authority because he feels he is being punished by them. Understanding the delinquent along with his social environment seems to have more effective and lasting results. Like any other behavior problem, delinquency can be the result of inconsistency in parents in giving affection and praise.

Delinquent behavior in college involves the minor violation of moral and legal codes. There is no college or university that does not expel or place on conduct probation students who violate college regulations or who commit offenses that are punishable by the laws of the college and society. Unless they suffer from psychosis, delinquent students are considered mentally competent, as they know the difference between right and wrong. Therefore, should they behave contrary to established rules they are responsible for, they suffer the consequences of such behavior. Some students of this type are asked, under administrative pressure, to seek professional consultations if the prognosis is good; others are advised, for their own benefit, to make use of any available mental health facilities in the community. In the treatment of the delinquent, the philosophy is always humane. Delinquent behavior is not innate but mostly learned.

The student who breaks or neglects college regulations often tries to act more important than he really is in order to feel superior. He overestimates himself, and he underestimates others. The college world appears threatening to him because he feels unable to work within the college framework; he feels unsuitable, a misfit. He finds cooperation a difficult task, and he wants to avoid it. This kind of student tries to elevate himself by deception: he labels law-abiding and conforming students as being weak, cowards, and "chicken." Since he feels neglected and out of place, he finds it easier to blame them than himself. Thus, he develops a mistaken image of himself. Some students act this way, occasionally; but if such a faulty self-image is too rigid, he cannot survive in college. By falsely heightening his personal worth to avoid duties, he is merely deluding himself.

Delinquency in college is different in scope and intensity than in society, but the principle and the motives can be the same. The reason why delinquent behavior is being presented here is that students do have occasional phantasies of wishing to violate college regulations (drinking, speeding, cheating, forgery), but their conscience is strong enough to keep these thoughts from materializing. One of the main reasons for the student to refrain from violating college rules, besides that of his conscience, is that unlawfulness in college will invariably have an effect on his status as a student; it may force him to withdraw from the college environment, although his act of violation may not have been punishable by society's rules. Being in college poses a double jeopardy which necessitates greater control of impulses, if the student desires a successful and relatively troublefree college career.

## Alcoholism

At times delinquent and sociopathic behavior can be manifested in alcoholic intoxication. Although the classical alcoholic is quite uncommon in the college population, there are some students who consume more than the minimum that is socially tolerated and legally acceptable for the student's age. Many students are social drinkers. For them, alcohol is conducive to a free and smooth flow of conversation, and it reduces their social anxiety and shyness—a characteristic that is common to many college students who did not engage in extensive social activities before coming to the campus. Drinking is often a crutch for personal insecurity. Students who are prone to use alcohol in excess often feel unloved, lonely, cannot deal with unpleasant situations, and have not recognized their personal limitations. They may be dependent and passive persons who lack drive and become easily discouraged when faced with demanding and stressful situations, and are looking for an easy way to avoid them.

The occasional use of alcohol for social reasons (cocktails, dinners), provided that the student is of legal age, is acceptable as long as his purpose in drinking is to be sociable, and not to become inebriated. In other words, if the motive to drink stems primarily from the pleasure that one derives from being with others, and if the alcoholic beverage is a secondary occasion, then these reasons cause no harm to the student. It is when the student seeks alcoholic drinks mainly in order to feel its soothing and tranquilizing effects that an emotional problem may be present. Everyone knows that when one is slightly tense or frustrated he may take refuge in a small amount of alcohol. In fact, many adults employ this habit but practically never have any difficulty; they realize that the consequences of the drinking habit are much more serious than the present symptoms from which they seek relief. Hence, they cease drinking as soon as the slight effects of alcohol are felt. The reason why adolescents should be discouraged from drinking is because they may not be mature enough to know when to discontinue.

Alcoholism usually denotes an underlying personality problem. The college student may rely on alcohol in order to be able to face the ordinary academic demands. Many severe alcoholics are neurotic, although this degree is rarely found in college students. When treatment has abated the drinking habit, there is often a relapse simply because the emotional problem responsible for the alcoholic indulgence is not eliminated. Chronic alcoholism may be associated with brain tissue damage which cannot be restored. Such persons suffer from loss of memory, lose contact from reality, and become mentally deteriorated. Those alcoholics who are somewhat less advanced in their addiction frequently lose their judgment and reaction time, and become easily aggressive, depressed, or excited, and cannot control themselves. Alcohol does not stimulate the person; it weakens his control so that his real thoughts, feelings, and emotions are expressed with less personal restriction and censorship. This is why the student, by consuming alcohol, can easily become involved in areas where academic discipline is concerned.

Excessive drinking stems more from psychological factors than from any other reasons. The most important ones are presented here: (1) The student who is socially inhibited may become attracted to alcohol because it has disinhibiting effects. He finds it easier to talk more freely and with less sensitivity to people; his confidence is temporarily boosted. (2) Anxiety, fear, and depression can be temporarily lessened with alcohol, although the after-effects later on may make him feel worse. (3) The student who feels inadequate, inferior, and less masculine often erroneously associates alcohol with roughness, aggressiveness, and with masculinity; he uses alcohol to allow expression of his pent-up aggressive tendencies and the consequences can be blamed on the alcohol, not on himself. He tends to look upon those who abstain from alcohol as being prudish and "weak" persons, which is perhaps the same way he feels about himself but is unwilling to face it because it is painful to him. (4) Finally, alcohol can be a means to elicit attention and pity from those with whom the student has not been able to relate well.

There are several drugs on the market that can be used as an adjunct in the treatment of the alcoholic student. However, these drugs aim primarily at breaking the habit of drinking. The best way is to help him uncover the real cause for his need to drink excessively. The successful treatment of alcoholism demands the involvement of many therapeutic modalities including medical treatment, support from social agencies, and from Alcoholics Anonymous. Seldom is the treatment fully successful if only one of the above methods is used. Although psychotherapy is indicated in nearly all cases, many persons cannot profit to the same extent from such therapy. The alcoholic student who will most likely benefit from psychotherapy, regardless of whether drugs are administered to him, is the one who desires to recover, and who is capable of understanding why he drinks. He must have the capacity for recovery, and the stamina to sustain himself without alcohol for a considerable period of time. The goal of psychotherapy is frequently to help the alcoholic student find a new workable life situation which provides satisfactions that are greater than drinking.

## Homosexual Behavior

One of the types of personality disorders is homosexuality. It means that the aim of the sexual urge, in the broad sense of the word, is toward a member of the same sex. This tendency is considered normal behavior during the childhood years when there is greater socialization with members of the same sex, and heterosexual awakening has not yet taken place. But with the onset of adolescence, the focus of sexuality changes toward the opposite sex. Hence, if this heterosexual stage is not reached, it implies that the individual is still behaving in the childhood manner, and he has not made the change, through social learning, to the heterosexual role. A distorted image of one's self, cultural pressure, and fear of and resentment toward the opposite sex seem to be the main causes for lack of heterosexual development.

Homosexuality is more prevalent in males than in females. Such behavior most frequently begins during adolescence. The homosexual feels isolated from his parents, but when forced to choose between them he feels closer to his mother, for he sees the father as passive and rejecting. In many instances, the parents present him with a considerable confusion in identity as far as the masculinity-femininity conflict is concerned. More frequent is the case of the student who occasionally experiences impulses, dreams, and phantasies of homosexual content, and who becomes anxious because of his feelings and attitudes about himself as being "feminine." Concern over masturbation, doubts about sexual potency, and uncertainty in playing the masculine role are not uncommon feelings among students. Also, there are some who have been through incidental homosexual behavior of an experimental nature during puberty, but have mostly outgrown this pattern by the time they reach college age. These students should realize that it is unnecessary for them to worry over such past behavior.

When the male student regards himself as a "sissy," he may have been exposed to hostile and misinformed peers who put doubts in his mind. Another reason is that some of the ordinary college activities which he happens to enjoy are looked upon by others as indicative of an effeminate trend (music, art, poetry). Another factor that seems to be significant is the possibility of the student having a dominant mother and a passive father. Such a mother cultivates high expectations for the student which he feels he must fulfill if he is going to be a capable and masterful male. If he fails, he may have strong misgivings about his masculinity; the situation worsens if the father happens to be a basically weak and dependent person because the male student will acquire a faulty male identification, and he may have difficulty competing with other males and relating to the female.

The student must bear in mind that the relationship described above does not logically work in reverse. For instance, if the student looks upon his father as a passive individual and his mother as being more dominant than the father, he should not conclude that he must necessarily have problems related to lack of masculine identity. Every student has had parents who have been occasionally rejecting and unpleasant to him; furthermore, these factors alone are never sufficient to cause the student a faulty social and emotional development. It is the student's own attitude toward his parents' behavior, and the extent to which he *allows* them to influence him that determines how he will develop. The outlook for changing his behavior becomes favorable as soon as he realizes that he, himself, is more responsible for his condition than are his parents.

Homosexuality can be treated with psychotherapy just as any other type of deviant behavior. The chances for some students to make the change toward heterosexual behavior are good, because many are still adolescents, who experience frustration and isolation and are motivated to change. If there was something unusual in his family relationships which prevented the student from reorienting his sexual interests, and if he feels a little anxious about his deviation and has a desire to change, then the prognosis is good. Dreams and phantasies of a homosexual nature, a "crush" on a member of the same sex, admiration for the masculine physique, are not necessarily pathological, and the student is not labeled as homosexual if he has them. Nor are feminine physique and/or mannerisms in males related to homosexual behavior. However, if the student becomes too anxious about these feelings and thoughts, he can find relief and assurance by discussing them with a counselor or a therapist.

Every male student has both heterosexual and homosexual drives, but in nearly all cases, the former is dominant over the latter. Therefore, when the student experiences an occasional dream or impulsive thought of a homosexual nature he need not panic or become anxious if he recognizes that this process can occasionally happen to every perfectly normal male. This phenomenon simply means that the homosexual impulse for a moment became stronger than the heterosexual one, and in most cases it lasts only temporarily. A similar occurrence is the student's incidental desire to have a homosexual encounter to decide if he is actually homosexual. He may be simultaneously fearful that once he indulges in such activity he will become a homosexual for the remainder of his life. Most students who experiment usually feel "disgusted" afterwards, and find heterosexual experiences more gratifying and rewarding.

        ✻    ✻    ✻    ✻

In the course of treatment for personality disorders, the student is urged to understand what the factors in his personality are that press him to act in these ways. Some students are able to perceive quickly the mechanics of their personality that trigger their behavior. Then they are able to recount in an historical fashion, the events of their earlier life that may have formed the patterns and traits. Conditions in their current situation which may aggravate their behavior are also explored. As the students can more easily understand and evaluate their behavior, they recognize the undesirable aspects of their actions and, with the guidance of the therapist, are introduced to better alternatives that will give them lasting satisfaction. Since personality disorders are formed from childhood, it may sometimes be rather difficult for students to change, even if they do understand themselves. Therefore, for many students, treatment seldom changes their personality, but merely weakens the personality disorder enough so that they may function with more ease.

The categories of maladjustment presented in this chapter are not the only existing classifications. However, along with those discussed in the preceding chapter, they constitute the largest portion of the emotional problems found in the college student. Some of the remaining categories include those students who revert to childish behavior when easily frustrated, who are emotionally inadequate to meet minor stress situations, and who respond to the world in a way that indicates that a severe, unfortunate incident happened early in their lives which prevents them from acting normally. Other categories include those students who experience severe mood shifts (mild changes of mood are normal), and who exhibit incompatible and unstable personalities. It must also be mentioned that each of these categories of emotional difficulty has more subcategories which, because of their great detail, are beyond the scope of the present book. For more extensive information on the classification of these problems, the student should consult a text on abnormal psychology.

# 7

## MENTAL HEALTH PERSONNEL AND
## TREATMENT METHODS

**M**OST EDUCATIONAL INSTITUTIONS which maintain a dispensary or health service department are aware of the fact that a troubled mind may precipitate physical symptoms. The student first visits the physician, who may discover that the origin of the physical complaints are due to a mental and emotional condition. He could also be referred by a dean or member of the academic staff to the personnel in mental health for evaluation. The mental health team in this instance usually does not have final authority but acts in an advisory capacity. If the institution does not maintain such specialized service, the student can be referred to facilities in the local community. The health service or dispensary physician is in a position to make this decision and to undertake the procedures for the proper referral. There are, however, minor variations in these procedures from one educational institution to another. The professional workers in the field of mental health, and their duties and methods of treatment, are described in the following pages.

The college student who may want to seek assistance for any problem which he is likely to encounter in college will come in contact with any of the following workers in the mental health field: psychiatrist, clinical psychologist, counselor, and psychiatric social worker. Although not all academic institutions have such professional persons, large universities will have all of these types, and smaller colleges may employ one or two such members. It will be helpful for the college student to know something about their professional responsibilities and the types of service they offer. Many of their duties and treatment methods overlap; however, there is some basis for distinction among these professional persons which should be helpful to the student when he has to make a choice of the proper person for his particular problem.

### Psychiatrist

The psychiatrist is a doctor of medicine who specializes in psychiatry. His training requires five years of specialized instruction after he has earned his M.D. degree. During the first three years of this training period, he studies under direct supervision in an accredited institution, and in the following two years, he receives more experience by dealing directly with psychiatric patients. After this training, he is eligible for examination by the American Board of Psychiatry and Neurology, which certifies him as a specialist in psychiatry. He becomes an accredited member of the Board after he passes a written and oral examination. Being a physician, he is qualified to administer drugs and other medical therapies. In the past, the psychiatrist was more closely associated with hospitalized patients who had severe mental illnesses. Today, he offers his service to normal people everywhere, in clinics, welfare organizations, and in colleges and universities, as a consultant and educator in preventive psychiatry and in the promotion of mental health.

If a student's mental or emotional state is suspected to be of an organic nature, then it is the psychiatrist who is qualified to examine and treat the student if indicated. Should the college physician suspect an emotional difficulty behind the physical symptoms, he may refer the student to a psychiatrist or psychologist. To rule out the possibility of organic factors, the psychiatrist may perform a physical or a neurological examination. He may order laboratory tests and x-rays if they are indicated. The psychiatrist is able to make a diagnosis based on his findings. His treatment methods may be only with drugs, with psychotherapy, or with both simultaneously. Of these, the third alternative is more acceptable in current psychiatric practice. Should a psychiatrist have difficulty establishing a diagnosis on his initial contact with the student, he may refer him on to the clinical psychologist, who will administer a battery of tests in order to elicit more unconscious factors that may be responsible for the student's problems.

The importance of preventive psychiatry in the educational efforts to promote and maintain mental health in college has become recognized in recent years. Essentially, prevention entails guidance and reorientation of the student so that he can meet with the problems of adjustment and solve them in the most effective way. Prevention attempts not only to prevent the problems from occurring, but also to decide what to do about them after they occur. The psychiatrist, therefore, should be looked upon as an educator and advisor—not a "head doctor," as he is still referred to by many laymen. Should the student have doubts about a certain emotional area in his life, and if he worries excessively about something which disturbs him, he can consult a psychiatrist, as he does any ordinary medical doctor concerning a physical ailment.

Years ago, people visited a dentist only because of intolerable pain, and a physician was called only when the patient did not improve with practical remedies. Likewise, the psychiatrist was consulted only when someone became visibly "crazy" by the layman's standards. Today, except for the psychiatrist, the practice has changed. People visit the dentist and physician on the basis of routine check-ups when no symptoms are present. This new emphasis has been termed *preventive* medicine, which aims at the prevention of a disorder long before it becomes a real problem. Unfortunately, preventive psychiatry has not yet become popular, and people still visit the psychiatrist only when they have a current problem that bothers them. Some mental hygienists predict that within the next few decades, the periodic psychiatric check-up will become a routine matter, as it is with the physician and dentist today.

## Clinical Psychologist

Psychology is a large field which is generally and theoretically committed to the scientific study of human behavior. Educational, experimental, physiological, social, developmental, statistical, and comparative psychology are a few examples which show the diversity of the field. Clinical psychology is the largest segment of these specializations; nearly one third of all psychologists are in the clinical area. Clinical psychology deals mostly with the individual's behavior regarding his emotions, feelings, and thoughts insofar as they either disturb him or appear out of the ordinary from the viewpoint of others. Although the clinical psychologist has a strong background in research methods and in the scientific approach toward the study of human behavior, he also is interested in the causes of maladaptive behavior, and he establishes diagnoses and treats those with emotional problems. In other words, clinical psychology renders services, and is considered a science *and* a profession.

The clinical psychologist holds a Doctor of Philosophy (Ph.D.) degree in clinical psychology. The Ph.D. degree is earned with four to five years of graduate work following the B.A. degree. An additional year is spent as an intern in a clinic or mental hospital, where he receives practical training under close supervision. After five years of practice as a clinician, he is eligible for a diploma which makes him a Diplomate in clinical psychology. It is awarded by the American Board of Examiners in Professional Psychology after he successfully completes rigorous oral and written examinations, and it serves as a sign of professional distinction. Some clinical psychologists terminate their training with an M.A. degree; however, their responsibilities and duties are more limited than those with the doctoral degree.

The clinical psychologist utilizes psychological tests in order to appraise the emotional and intellectual status of the individual's personality. Broadly speaking, there are two types of clinical tests used with students. The first is *subjective* tests, which have ambiguous stimuli (inkblots, vague pictures of people) that the student is asked to *interpret*. By doing so, he unknowingly reveals aspects of his personality. Thus, the psychologist or counselor is able to understand the student's deeper layers of his personality, and as the student learns about himself, the counselor is better able to help him. The second type is *objective* tests, which consist mainly of questions asking factual information about his past experiences, his thoughts, and his feelings. A battery of both types of tests is normally used, but the tests of each type can vary according to the nature of the problems. Subjective tests are more apt to be used with emotional difficulties; objective tests are more likely to be used with problems of a vocational nature.

The results of these tests help the therapist to know what to do with a student who has a particular problem. By knowing certain personal characteristics, he is thus able to concentrate on the proper areas of maladjustment, and he can assist the student more effectively. He does not treat the symptoms, but through the interpretation of psychological tests he searches for the reasons of the symptoms. With the use of these tests, the clinical psychologist assesses and predicts the student's behavior. As with the psychiatrist, the clinical psychologist also serves as a consultant to the members of the academic staff.

## Counseling Psychologist

Counseling psychology is a broad term which deals with a number of problems typical of the college student, but not ordinarily of a severe nature. Everyone is already familiar with the term "counselor" as it applies to the vocational counselor, the guidance counselor, etc. These persons are psychologists primarily trained in helping students with problems of a vocational nature, or with a variety of other problems which do not result from a disorganized personality. The years of training and degrees earned are essentially the same for them as for the clinical psychologist, except that their emphasis is more on the student's immediate situation and his future and vocational choice. The counseling psychologist normally does not probe into the deeper, unconscious facets of the student's personality, but, instead, he guides him vocationally, he estimates his aptitudes and interests, and he helps him with his current academic load, and with problems related to his social adaptation.

Counseling psychologists usually work in guidance and vocational orientation centers where they help students in choosing a career realistically. They are skilled in the interpretation of a variety of tests, ranging from general intellectual ability, to areas of special aptitude and interests. By discovering the student's strong interests and abilities, he can guide the student toward a career in which he is suited and most likely to succeed. Many difficulties in college students are not purely vocational, but are also psychological. Hence, the counselor or counseling psychologist often engages in treating the student for his emotional problems. His professional responsibilities may overlap with those of the clinical psychologist.

Because the counseling psychologist works mostly as an educational and vocational-guidance expert, a considerable amount of his work consists of interpreting the results of aptitude, interest, and intelligence tests, and of measuring the student's level and area of adjustment. He can uncover deficiencies in specific academic areas and can recommend special courses and guidance problems. He advises staff members and various counselors who may need information as they guide the student's academic and social conduct. To the student who is failing he may point out where special academic skills are needed. He can determine the student's capabilities and his motivation to pursue his goals. He can recommend the need for changing a student's attitude, and even the benefits of psychotherapy can be suggested, if indicated to be necessary for the student. With the aid of expert guidance at the college level, the student can save himself unnecessary difficulty in later life.

Vocational counselors are usually available to the student to help him explore the great variety of fields and professions that are open to him, before he declares his vocational intentions. These counselors can help the student arrive at a choice of profession which is consistent with his talents, and avoid pitfalls and mistakes should he happen to lack experience or maturity to make the proper choice himself. There have been many instances where time and money were used unwisely on the wrong choice of a vocation, for going into a field for the wrong reasons. On a few occasions, a student who is about to graduate realizes he has been in the wrong field, and wishes he knew more about what he should expect, prior to making the choice of his profession. All these problems can be avoided if the student takes advantage of the counseling facilities in his college.

## Psychiatric Social Worker

A new field whose importance is becoming more recognized today as an essential part of the mental health team in many colleges and universities is psychiatric social work. After receiving his M.A. degree from an accredited school of social work, which requires about two years of training beyond the B.A. degree including supervised instruction, the psychiatric social worker becomes an important aide for the psychiatrist. For example, he can obtain information about a student by interviewing persons who are close to or who know him well, usually with the student's permission. He collects from reliable and pertinent sources any information that may be valuable to the psychiatrist. In many instances he interviews the student first and he prepares the information so that the psychiatrist will know in advance the student's problem.

The psychiatric social worker in college can help the student with a variety of social and adjustment problems, and he can assist him in overcoming temporary obstacles. If warranted by the situation, he often can talk with parents about the student's problems, as well as with counselors and members of the academic staff on matters ranging from an academic to a social nature. He often serves as a liaison between the mental health team and the community or parents. He can help the student in making constructive decisions which will concern the student after he leaves college. The psychiatric social worker is skilled in obtaining detailed childhood histories, he may study the home situation and discuss with parents their own attitude toward the student, and he may give the student support and confidence. Finally, he can help the student by making environmental changes (home, college), and by guiding him toward immediate and realistic goals.

## Characteristics of Therapists

All four workers in the field of mental health in college can be regarded as therapists, and since each shares in helping the student deal with his problems, many of their functions overlap. Therapy can vary from a few sessions to many months of sessions, depending on the nature of the difficulty. These therapists do not judge, criticize, or preach to the student. Neither do they become emotionally involved with the student's problem. Furthermore, they do not "cure" the student of his symptoms, nor do they use "suggestion" on him. In a general way, they guide him so that he is enabled to help himself. Therapists do not avoid a student socially, nor downgrade him or treat as an inferior and weak human being the student who has emotional problems, any more than does a physician whose patients are afflicted with physical ailments.

Therapists who work with students have certain common personal characteristics which enable them to be effective in their work. They exhibit sensitivity to the needs and feelings of the student, and they are trained to provide a permissive atmosphere in the psychotherapy session, in which the student can express himself freely without fear of humiliation and rejection, regardless of how "bad" the student feels when he expresses his feelings. Their approach in helping the student is not always the same; other factors, such as the duration of the problem, the intensity, and the type of problem are always considered. This implies that these therapists are interested first in listening to the student's problem so that all the facts and feelings are aired. As the student relates his problem in detail, the therapist, in his own mind, begins to conceptualize the situation taking into account all the pertinent data.

The members of the mental health team in the college or university are interested in the causes behind the presenting symptoms, the early emotional experiences of the student, the way he perceives his current environment, and his aims and expectations of the future. These personal experiences along with his family background, desires, thoughts, and feelings are areas of a personal nature to be explored in confidence. The psychiatrist and psychologists do not interrogate the student, and do not compile the information in order to use it against him. They are interested in discovering the real motives and in helping him develop a satisfying and useful life. Psychotherapy does not "cure" the person, in the strict sense of the word, but it aims to help him live a more creative and productive life, and to enable him to learn to face stress with a minimum of disabling symptoms.

The psychologist and psychiatrist, on campus or in the university community, should be looked upon as educators and consultants. In most instances with students, the task of these workers is to avert emotional crises before they occur, or to treat the milder emotional problems at a time when the student is still developing emotionally and intellectually and has good capacity to understand himself, and when aspects of his personality are easier to modify because they have not fully crystallized. Workers in mental health do not treat "crazy" people, as some misinformed laymen still believe although this may have been true a century ago when knowledge and facilities were not as available as in our modern times. Today the aim of these workers is to forestall the possibility of emotional disorganization in the student, just as he undergoes physical and dental checkups to avoid serious ailments.

The student should not expect the psychologist and psychiatrist to be immune from conflicts; nor are these professional people always able to apply their knowledge in the solving of their own problems. They, too, may require professional consultation from their colleagues, just as a physician must see another physician for a physical examination. In fact, during their training they receive varying amounts of therapy, depending on their personality, in order to become more aware of their own weaknesses and traits so that these traits do not interfere with their treatment of the problems of other persons. No one is ever expected to eradicate completely the occurrence of conflicts, since they are typical of normal life. The important thing is how the student is able to deal with them after they occur.

## Psychotherapy

Psychotherapy is a broad term, the meaning of which may range from giving simple advice to the probing of unconscious forces. Psychotherapeutic treatment varies with the age of the subject, and it is not always completely effective. There are many treatment methods, but some are more suitable for a special kind of case than are other forms of treatment. Consequently, the therapist may vary his procedure until he finds the one that has the greatest effect upon the student. The same procedure is often followed by the physician who may change the dosage and the type of antibiotics until he discovers the one with the best results. Students with the same type of problem usually do not respond equally well to the same form of psychotherapy.

There is a distinction between counseling and psychotherapy, although these terms are often used interchangeably. The former method usually is of a shorter duration, and it is used particularly to solve immediate problems and to offer support for stressful situations. It assists the student in formulating realistic goals, in becoming more productive in his work, and in gaining a truer perspective of himself. On the other hand, psychotherapy is used with deeper and more incapacitating problems, and it aims at changing the student's personality, no matter to how small a degree. It aids the student by analysing his behavior and synthesizing the components of his personality in a reintegrative fashion. Such a process is utilized for problems of a more serious nature. For example, a student who feels tense and shy and is unable to talk when in social groups may only require brief counseling. But a student who has severe depression accompanied by bizarre thoughts and attempts to commit suicide will normally require psychotherapy. Neither psychotherapy nor counseling changes the individual into a new and completely different human being any more than does an automobile become new after it has been repaired.

It is more important for the student to become aware of a characteristic in his personality, than to know exactly how, why, and when it started. An analogous example is a case of acute appendicitis. The surgeon will proceed immediately with the operation and be successful without even knowing the specific causes. It should be noted that the student does not become worse if psychotherapy makes him aware of the real causes of his problem. Once a psychological problem has been solved and the student's emotions and thought processes are in good order, he can be helped to explore further the related causes in order to prevent the possibility of recurrence.

Several techniques are used in therapy depending on the nature of the problem, on the basic structure of the student's personality, on his desire to improve and on the severity and intensity of the conflict. Since college students are comparatively well-integrated, are intelligent, express themselves relatively well, and, by expending some effort, are able to think through many of their situational problems, the therapist encourages the student to work out his psychological problem by himself. This and other methods of psychotherapeutic technique are illustrated in the following case.

A twenty-two-year-old male student had requested to see an older, experienced, and mature therapist. He complained of depression and bewilderment about the injustices in the world, and he expressed dissatisfaction with college and lack of motivation. He had been unable to decide on the choice of a career, always vacillating between law and psychology. The student was sarcastic towards professors and hostile to those who held prestige professions. His parents were divorced when he was three years old, and since then he had met the father, who was a prominent lawyer, only a few times. The student never got along well with the step-father.

From this information the therapist can select the most important event, make a brief comment, and focus the student's attention on it. The therapist might say, "You can't make up your mind what you really want to do." The therapist may also sum up many significant events and interpret or reflect them back to the student so that the student becomes aware of patterns of behavior which are not conducive to adjustment. He may say to the student, "You seem to be looking for a father substitute, and you feel resentful for not having a real father." Finally, the therapist can help the student gain insights by pointing out meaningful relationships between events of which the student was not aware. He may say, for example, "You did not get along well with your step-father and you have difficulty relating to staff members. Could it be that you resent all father-figures?"

After the student states his problem as *he* sees and understands it, and expresses his feelings about it, he is encouraged to delve into other areas about which the therapist may want to know in order to evaluate his problem more correctly. He may want to know, for example, how the student related with his peers during his childhood, with what parent is he closer, what are their personality characteristics, what was happening at the time of the onset of his difficulties, and many other factors which can vary according to the nature of the problem. The therapist with his indirect probing and observation of the student's behavior in the office can identify the student's main mechanism of defense and the manner in which he copes with stress. He can also discover the student's main weaknesses and areas where improvement is needed.

Surprisingly enough, some students gain such insight and relief after having stated their problem in the first interview, that they no longer find it necessary for further appointments. Simply stating and recognizing his problem can in itself be therapeutic for the student. The majority of students who seek help for emotional problems derive noticeable benefit from only a few sessions.

However, the therapist does not perform miracles. By way of exploration he helps the student to identify the source of his problem; the student is made to see the situation clearly as it really exists. Although the student is not expected simply to unload his problems on the therapist's lap, often, the expression of emotions and feelings becomes necessary, especially if the student has no other place to ventilate them. The method of treatment of emotional problems is not the same as with the physical illnesses. In the latter case, the patient is not expected to do very much; the physician or surgeon does all of the work. In solving emotional problems, the student is expected to be much more active than the therapist.

An optimistic prognosis for recovery depends upon the student's level of motivation. The therapist's role is to nudge and guide the student towards recovery. If the student shows concern with his problem and displays a genuine desire to eliminate it, and if he is aware that he himself will be the one to bring about a change in himself, he will eventually achieve some degree of success. It is considered the student's and not the therapist's success. Prognosis depends on the type, severity, and length of the problem. Students with severe maladjustment and who are no longer mentally competent and responsible for their behavior are usually asked to withdraw from school, to seek hospitalization or long term treatment elsewhere.

The student is held accountable for the carrying out of the decisions and goals reached mutually with his therapist. The latter does not tell the student what to do except for special instances that warrant direct advice. The student is assisted in seeing the nature of his difficulty and in solving it in an effective way. The aim of psychotherapy with respect to the student's problems is to correct faulty attitudes and to enhance a realistic outlook on life.

The student usually acts according to what he thinks of himself. His ideas about himself, however, may not be too accurate, and the therapist can help him re-evaluate himself, after everything has been taken into account and appraised with a minimum of subjectivity, so that he can function within the limits of his abilities. Of course, the student can still strive for betterment as long as his aims are not too far out of the reach of his capacities. However, some students have such high vocational aspirations that they soon become disillusioned because they did not take into account the availability of the necessary intellectual resources and the work that would be involved.

The trained therapist has a good knowledge of the theory of personality, and he has experience with the techniques of psychotherapy and counseling. He is able to perceive the problem quickly, and he helps the student to become involved with himself and with academic and social tasks, as much as his abilities will allow. The student is discouraged from using too intellectual terms which are remote from and have little to do with the way he feels, or to discuss a third party who has only an indirect connection with the student's problem. A fuller understanding of the student's problem is achieved by helping him to think and perceive his situation clearly, to express his feelings about it, and to label his feelings accurately.

The ultimate goals of psychotherapy are to make the student adapt to his environment, become more efficient socially and academically, and be able to achieve his personal goals. These goals are forwarded by having the student work out his own solutions to his problems provided that the therapist clarifies to the student the positive and negative tendencies in his personality. Sometimes, the clearing up of misconceptions and doubts is in itself a removal of interfering stress. At other times, when the student's attention is diverted from excessive pre-occupation with inner problems into social activities, his symptoms diminish considerably. The greater his insight about himself, the easier it will be for him to utilize constructive techniques which will eventually eliminate his symptoms.

The most important aspect of preventive psychiatry today in colleges and universities is how to cope with emotional problems in their earlier stages which, if left untreated could precipitate a more serious condition. One of the recent trends in college health is the orientation of student counselors and staff members so that they can detect and recognize the overt emotional problems of the student. Here is the most effective value of the psychiatrist and psychologist in college. The restoration of balance and order in the student's life so that he can satisfy his personal needs while promoting those of his society, and the integration of the values of his milieu into his personality are processes experienced through learning. For even the treatment of the emotional problems is essentially a more sophisticated form of re-education. Many of the student's emotional problems, however, are of little consequence and can be taken care of with relatively minor effort by the student himself, or with a minimum of nonprofessional help.

The student more frequently expresses the need to understand himself better when things are not working out well for him. The greater the amount of difficulty he encounters, the more he wants to learn about himself. Self-understanding is achieved to a considerable degree by providing the student with an atmosphere in which he can state his conflicts and feelings verbally. This process leads him into expressing his emotions which up to this time he kept harnessed. The therapist can help the student express his ill feelings without the fear that he will be rejected or ridiculed. The student is encouraged to say the unpleasant things which he always kept to hmiself. After the unpleasant problem has been exposed and evaluated, the student is helped to recognize solutions and to gain insight about the possible causes. The student himself must be motivated for change, and the therapist points out the direction in which the change can take place. However, the student must understand the whole problem before he can be prepared to cope with it.

When the student's expectations of college are too high or unrealistic he is apt to feel some stress. While many students overcome such difficulties through their association with friends and colleagues, there are always a few who will find it difficult to resolve the stress without suffering personal discomfort. Despite their personal efforts to understand the basis for their difficulty, they are unable to find better methods for handling their problems. Thus, some students with social, personal, or academic problems will experience difficulty handling them when they experiment with trial-and-error techniques, and when they follow the advice of other, inexperienced students. However, the therapist can help the student use more satisfying ways to deal with his problem areas without the necessity of effecting a drastic change in the student's personality, or having to take unnecessary measures (quit school, drop courses).

The student should be aware that it is quite possible for him to recover from a transient difficulty without ever receiving any professional help. Furthermore, not all students with problems need to see a clinical psychologist or psychiatrist. Clergymen, parents, members of the academic staff, and even a "good friend" who is capable of listening to the student sympathetically can be of benefit to him. Sometimes, however, he may not realize the severity of his problem as he seeks aid from nonprofessional persons. Hence, it would be better for the student to see a specialist in mental health at the onset of his difficulty, thus saving time and painful efforts even if the problem turns out to be of minimal importance. The student with ineffective study habits, social immaturity and shyness, sensitivity to authority, and an inability to express himself, does not necessarily have psychiatric problems. In many cases, these patterns of behavior are automatically outgrown. Those who suffer from such problems, however, should take advantage of competent assistance.

It frequently happens that, when the student realizes he must improve his study methods, change his attitudes, and acquire a healthier feeling toward college, he is prone to convince himself of his inadequacy and to feel that he "should have known better." Everyone can benefit from improvement—even the exceptional student. The real issue is whether the individual takes advantage of the available resources. It is as unrealistic to think of a student without the need for guidance as it is to think that a statesman does not need advisors. The matter becomes of concern only when the student constantly needs to be coaxed to perform adequately, or if he depends on others for even minute problems. Nearly everyone needs the assistance, from time to time, of a specialist if he is going to attain success. It is, therefore, necessary for the student to avoid both excessive autonomy and strong dependency upon others.

Nearly all students will experience a feeling of defeat and a lack of enthusiasm some time during their college career. Some students will have these feelings more than others. In most instances, such feelings are temporary and disappear as soon as the student finds rewards for his work, as his accomplishments are appreciated by others, and as his activities take on meaning for himself. Otherwise, if these feelings are a source of constant worry, there may be deeper reasons based on his attitudes and on the basic characteristics of his personality.

Students who are without discernible emotional problems can still benefit from discussions with any of the workers in the mental health field. These workers do not "read peoples' minds" as is often believed by unsophisticated persons. Only sorcerers claim such feats. What they do notice is mostly what others who are not trained in this field notice in their behavior. Psychologists and psychiatrists do not look for hidden symptoms or try to discover a "complex." Their service in the college setting can be of immense value when they can clarify the student's misconceptions about himself and rectify his misunderstandings. A few students are curious as to whether they are "normal" while others want to know what the normal personality is like so that they can compare themselves to an ideal pattern. There is no such perfect representation to which everyone is to be compared and judged by.

All the student's records concerning his emotional problem are kept in strict confidence by his therapist. In nearly all colleges and universities the therapist does not reveal information about a student who contacted him for a mental health program to government agencies, industry, etc., unless the student authorizes his therapist, in writing, to do so. Even then, such reports about the student are usually brief and general. Deans, parents, roommates, and friends are not ordinarily informed of the student's problems unless his mental and emotional condition is a threat to himself and to others. In case of application for employment, psychiatric records are not held against the student. The prevailing policy is that his own welfare is the most important factor when conditions for employment are considered. Finally, if the student's records are used for research purposes, his identity is always protected.

## Therapy with Drugs

A relatively promising approach in the treatment of the physical symptoms in emotional disturbances is the use of new drugs as therapeutic adjuncts. Not all such symptoms, however, require therapy with drugs. Only the physician or psychiatrist can determine whether such drugs should be dispensed, since in some cases, the student would have to be observed for possible side effects, and the daily dosage may have to be changed. Despite how strongly the student may feel the need for drugs, they are not always recommended; furthermore, they can cause harm if not used properly and with discretion. Prolonged dependence on drugs alone is not a very wise way of treating a long-standing emotional problem. Reliance on drugs may indicate that the student is not willing to face the real issues involved in his emotional condition. The following case illustrates this point.

A male graduate student listed several complaints—not doing as well academically as he wished, not being as socially integrated as he thought was desirable, and not being intellectually creative and productive. He felt that socially he had no "real friends," that he was anxious in social situations,

and felt very inadequate because of it. He traced his un-
sociability to his inability to maintain a conversation, and this,
he said, was due to the fact that he really had "no personality,"
that there was really nothing to him. The student stated further
that he often felt depressed because of his "inadequacies,"
felt he was just marking time, worried about his future, and so
on. He hoped someone could help him. He read about "psychic
energizers" which were described as the medication to clear
up a number of problems. He felt that they might help to
straighten him out. He complained of a complete feeling of
futility. He mentioned moodiness, lack of purpose, inability to
concentrate, wandering tension, boredom, a feeling of hopelessness, and general unhappiness with life. He felt that there
was no particular promise that the future would be better.
The student recited his symptoms and his need for help using
almost pleading tones. He was told that short-term psychotherapy would be available to him, but not the medication
that he requested. He was told, also, that medication would be
prescribed only as indicated, and in his case it did not seem
to be indicated.

The student followed the recommended psychotherapy sessions, and he began to show considerable improvement without
the aid of drugs. Relief occurred as he began to realize that his
problems were part of his own personality, and that corrective
efforts had to come from within himself. He was encouraged to
concentrate on the reasons for his inability to visualize a future
for himself, and to describe what it was about himself that
prevented him from creating meaningful friendships and that
led him to believe he was worthless and helpless. As he understood himself realistically, he gained some insights and was
helped to experiment with solutions. Finally, he was able to
learn and adapt the successful solutions. At the end of the
psychotherapy sessions, he felt he knew where he was going in
life, and he accepted his weaknesses and made better use of his
strengths. His grades improved and he felt that he was an
accepted member of society.

Students who feel slightly anxious or depressed, empty,
listless, hostile, unmotivated for college work, etc., and who do
not know what is really bothering them may tend to rely on

medication to eradicate these symptoms, rather than to recognize them as by-products of an emotional-mental condition. The therapist can aid the student in finding out what is the cause of these symptoms, and help him do something about them, so that he can become a contented and effective student. It is only when these symptoms become too pronounced for any type of short-term therapy to be effective that medication is given. Drugs are usually administered with the hope that, once the symptoms lessen, psychotherapy may become more beneficial.

Drugs ameliorate the symptoms; they do not eliminate the etiology behind the symptoms. The usefulness of these drugs lies in enabling the student to profit more readily from psychotherapy and to gain insight into his problem when the interfering symptoms have been reduced. For example, the extremely anxious or depressed student can think clearly and can concentrate on his problem after receiving drugs. While these drugs are effective in many cases, there is some disagreement as to their permanency and universal utility. The philosophy of treatment with drugs is not only to lessen the symptoms temporarily, but with psychotherapy to help the student understand and solve the reasons for his symptoms. This principle is more often applied with chronic than with acute symptoms.

Many psychiatrists, today, believe that these drugs, when combined with psychotherapy, are the best method for handling the physical symptoms which accompany emotional problems (psychosomatic difficulties). The dosages of these drugs are usually adjusted to the needs of the individual, and occasionally a combination of drugs is prescribed. These drugs control the severe symptoms of anxiety and depression, so that the student is better able to respond with insights into the reasons for his anxiety and depression when he undergoes psychotherapy. The drugs are mostly corrective rather than curative, in the same way that insulin helps the diabetic patient, as it replaces temporarily a vital substance, but it does not actually cure the person. Finally, it should be stressed that these drugs are not dispensed without a prescription from a physician or psychiatrist.

The first group of drugs is referred to as *ataraxic* drugs, or "tranquilizers." They have a calming effect on those who are emotionally disturbed. Among the common tranquilizing drugs is *reserpine*. This is the chemical name given to the chemicals found in the juices of a shrub grown in India. It is known as snakeroot, and for thousands of years was boiled and consumed for its tranquilizing effects. Gandhi was known to have used this drug. *Chlorpromazine* is a synthetic drug, and it was developed by French chemists at about the same time as reserpine. The effects are the same, but there is some variation of its action on the nervous system. There are many new tranquilizing drugs now on the market under different commercial names, i.e., Miltown®, Compazine®, Librium®, etc.

Tranquilizing drugs constitute several groups and varieties, and each varies in potency. These drugs have a different action than sedatives, and they do not usually make the person feel sleepy and sluggish. They bring control and relief to chronically agitated, excitable, irritable, and overactive persons with a minimum of drowsiness, fatigue, or mental dullness. The tranquilizing drugs calm and relax the central nervous system, and the person still remains mentally alert and able to do his work with less tension. Moderate anxiety and an occasional feeling of tension which are not too bothersome do not normally require tranquilizing drugs. The physician is in the best position to determine whether drugs are indicated, after he has examined the student.

The second group involves the *anti-depressant* drugs; their effect is opposite to that of the tranquilizers. There are several types of anti-depressant drugs. Some of these are: Niamid®, Marplan®, Nardil®, Tofranil®, Deaner®, etc. In many cases, they are quite effective in relieving worry, sadness, sleeplessness, and depressions brought on by stress situations. They render the person more relaxed, restore his interest in the environment, and make him amenable to psychotherapy. The general effects of the anti-depressant drugs are that they elevate the person's mood, and increase his mental alertness by stimulating the central nervous system and by accelerating his reactions so that he becomes more active and responsible to his environment.

### Group Psychotherapy

Group psychotherapy with college students is a relatively

modern concept, and becoming more popular in many mental health clinics in colleges and universities. It consists mainly of a small group of students and a counselor discussing together problems of a similar nature. A good reason for using group therapy is that many students can be helped simultaneously. Group psychotherapy is particularly advantageous for those students whose problems are of a social nature. The logic behind group psychotherapy is that people do not develop problems in a vacuum, but through interaction with other persons and groups. Thus, the student who finds himself among other students who also are trying to work out their problems is much more easily motivated to solve his own. Problems which developed with members of his own famliy can be more easily resolved in the group situation, since it is quite possible that other members of the group can become symbolic substitute members of his own family. Group psychotherapy can help the shy and withdrawn student to gain confidence, and it can help the overly aggressive student to control himself better.

In the group situation, the student feels free to communicate his feelings, gains valuable information from other students, and receives encouragement to become more active and to deal with his conflicts. Should he happen to come from a maladjusted or too competitive a home environment, he can learn to feel more secure in the group as he finds a cooperative spirit in it, and he becomes less sensitive to others. Group psychotherapy may begin as a gripe session, but with the intuitive effort of the therapist, each student can gain insights that can change his attitudes and promote his feeling of responsibility. The group situation is democratic, nonthreatening, and somewhat permissive. The group is not controlled by the therapist, but generally the group as a whole controls its individual members.

Group psychotherapy is very helpful for students who feel isolated and who experience anxiety when they have to relate closely with other students. The psychotherapist can help the student in the group to mature faster as the student becomes closer to and feels part of the group; and as he learns to express and examine himself he acquires a sense of identity. Many college students resent taking advice from older persons; but they can modify effectively their attitudes and decisions by sharing the experiences of their peers in the group. Students who have been overprotected and pampered by their parents, or who have been without siblings, are apt to experience some interpersonal difficulty. In the group situation they can be easily encouraged to share their feelings, for they soon realize that the other students feel the same way as they do. Some even can propose solutions for the group to discuss and evaluate, and eventually the ideas can be accepted and applied. Group psychotherapy is basically a formal type of social re-education.

Each individual student in the group is afforded contact and exposure with other students and he finds an interpersonal situation which is close to real life. Group psychotherapy is especially helpful to the student who did not have the opportunity to experience the more normal kind of socialization. Each student is guided to examine his own behavior toward others, and he becomes less confused when he realizes that others have similar difficulties. Furthermore, he gains more self-esteem as he discovers that many of his peers think and feel as he does. This fact in itself may dispel the confusion that the student may have regarding his personal identity, his capabilities, and his worth as a human being.

# ANNOTATED BIBLIOGRAPHY
## Selected Readings

BELL, NORMAN T., et al.: *Introduction to College Life*. Boston: Houghton Mifflin, 1962. A collection of stimulating articles with viewpoints by various authors, dealing with the aims of higher education, student-teacher relationships, and development of values in the student. It discusses the transition from high school to college, some of the realistic expectations and opportunities in college, and the student's continuing education after leaving college. Although primarily written for the college freshman, it can be gainful for all class levels.

BENNETT, MARGARET E.: *Getting the Most Out of College*. New York: McGraw-Hill, 1957. The book presents guidelines for the development of proper study habits and self-understanding, and offers useful suggestions on what the student can expect from college, on how to apply himself, and on how to deal with peers and social situations. It discusses ideas on marriage, vocation, and life goals. Practical for all college levels.

BIER, WILLIAM C.: *The Adolescent: His Search for Understanding*. New York: Fordham University Press, 1963. Contains many illuminating articles on the period of adolescent growth and on the emotional and sexual adjustment of the college student. Vocational choice, peer group influences, delinquency, and the role of the mental health professions are also treated in the book. Best suited for upperclassmen and graduate students.

BLAINE, GRAHAM B., AND CHARLES C. MCARTHUR: *Emotional Problems of College Students*. New York: Appleton-Century-Crofts, 1961. A collection of articles written by experts on college mental health. They describe the manner in which patterns of personality problems emerge in the college student, factors associated with the inability to study, and how social and emotional disturbances can be diagnosed and treated effectively. There is emphasis on the identification and treatment of severe emotional illnesses in college students. Although written for persons in the mental health professions, the book is suitable for upperclassmen and graduate students.

CHANDLER, JOHN ROSCOE, et al.: *Successful Adjustment in College*. New York: Prentice-Hall, 1951. The book covers topics on understanding one's personality, on developing social adjustment, study skills, and proper attitudes toward a vocation, marriage, and a philosophy of life. It provides work problems and stimulates the student's thinking. An invaluable source for freshmen.

DiMICHAEL, SALVATORE G.: *Improving Personality and Study Skills in College*. Milwaukee: Bruce, 1951. The book deals with the development of efficient study techniques, critical thinking, realistic career orientation, improvement of social skills, and maintenance of physical health. It emphasizes the importance of achieving proper values, attitudes, basic life goals and principles, and of forming a philosophy of life. An excellent guide book for lowerclassmen.

DuBois, CORA: *Foreign Students and Higher Education in the United States*. Washington, D. C.: American Council on Education, 1956. Portions of the book contain some typical reactions of foreign students attending American institutions of higher learning. The social and psychological attitudes, and other factors affecting the international student are presented. Suitable for all levels in college and for the average reader.

EDDY, EDWARD D., JR. (ed.): *The College Influence on Student Character*. Washington, D. C.: American Council on Education, 1959. A study, through interviews and personal observations from visits to twenty universities, to determine the influence of academic training on student character. It attempts to evaluate student goals, religious beliefs, responsibility, and attitudes toward the academic and environmental aspects of the college campus. Suitable for all readers.

FARNSWORTH, DANA L.: *Mental Health in College and University*. Cambridge: Harvard University Press, 1957. The book deals with the need for improvement in college mental health programs, and proposes remedies for better facilities and therapeutic techniques in the treatment of the emotional problems of the college population. It clarifies the role of college mental health personnel in relation to the academic and student body and provides a description of the emotional attitudes, needs, and stresses of the college student. Although aimed at the academic, administrative and professional personnel, it can benefit the upperclassman and graduate student.

FUNKENSTEIN, DANIEL H. (ed.): *The Student and Mental Health*: *An International View*. Cambridge: Riverside Press, 1956. Contains the proceedings of the First International Conference on mental health problems of college students in other parts of the world. It presents the views of spokesmen from several countries. They discuss many of the typical emotional difficulties of college students in their respective countries, examine the cultural and environmental factors associated with maladaptive behavior in college, and propose methods of treatment. Adaptable to all college levels. Of particular interest to students of sociology.

GALLAGHER, J. ROSWELL, AND HERBERT I. HARRIS: *Emotional Problems of Adolescents.* New York: Oxford University Press, 1958. A simply-written and easily-understood source for understanding the adolescent's behavior and feelings. It covers anti-social behavior, the striving for independence, anxiety and physical symptoms, and problems related to the sexual drive and to academic failure. Although written for persons in the mental health professions, it can also be helpful to the college student.

GARRISON, ROGER H.: *The Adventure of Learning in College.* New York: Harper, 1959. The author describes vividly the thinking and the emotional undertones of the college student. He portrays convincingly the goals of education, the meaning of learning, the art of relating with parents and teachers, and what the student should expect from a college education. With literary style and feeling, the writer explains the deeper meaning of education. Very pleasant reading, expressively written. Excellent for students of all levels and the general public.

GOLDSEN, ROSE K., *et al.*: *What College Students Think.* New Jersey: D. Van Nostrand, 1960. Attempts to understand the psychological and sociological climate of the university, gathered from students through questionnaires. It investigates the students' political, economic, national, international, and religious attitudes and opinions. The book reports the students' feelings and attitudes toward the educational and fraternity systems on campus, aspects of dating, and choice of a career. Befitting college students of all levels, educators, and the general reader.

GROUP FOR THE ADVANCEMENT OF PSYCHIATRY: *The College Experience: A Focus for Psychiatric Research.* New York: Report No. 52, 1962. The report deals with the areas and problems where psychiatric research in the college setting is needed, identified as individual, interpersonal, developmental, and educational. The report examines the role of the psychiatrist on the college campus. Particularly suited for the researcher in mental health. Contains an extensive bibliography.

HABEIN, MARGARET L. (ed.): *Spotlight on the College Student.* Washington, D. C.: American Council on Education, 1959. A discussion by experts of aspects of student and faculty values, and of their mutual roles and relationships. It examines the usefulness of social studies and liberal education, the changing of values at different class levels, and such concepts as responsibility, conformity, stability of values, etc. Contains many challenging ideas. Fit for the college student and the general reader.

JACOB, PHILIP E.: *Changing Values in College.* New York: Harper, 1957. An extensive survey of students' values in college. It examines the impact of the college experience on the student's attitudes, beliefs and values as a function of instructor, method of instruction, curriculum, and the predominant pattern of the student's personality. A significant contribution in the study of value change. Contains a rich bibliography. Appropriate for all college levels.

JERSILD, ARTHUR T.: *When Teachers Face Themselves*. New York: Teachers College, Columbia University, 1955. Presents a brief but excellent and simply-written discourse explaining anxiety, loneliness, hostility, love and the search for meaning and self-understanding. The book is based on interviews and questionnaires. Although primarily written for the teacher, it can be very helpful to the advanced undergraduate student.

LANDIS, PAUL H.: *So This Is College*. New York: McGraw-Hill, 1954. The book deals effectively with the student's feelings of inferiority, desire for independence, the need for life goals, freedom and vocational choice, and with conflicts over familial and interpersonal situations. It provides study techniques and explores attitudes toward parents and marriage, with information on self-understanding and sexual adjustment. Appropriate for all college levels and particularly lowerclassmen.

NIXON, ROBERT E.: *The Art of Growing*. New York: Random House, 1962. A guide for psychological growth, and for understanding and resolving dependency needs, identity diffusion, and conflicts with parents. It explains the steps of psychosexual development and emotional maturation, and the emotions of anxiety and anger. A good supplement to psychology courses. Best suited for the sophisticated upperclassman and graduate student.

RAUSHENBUSH, ESTHER: *The Student and His Studies*. Middletown: Wesleyan University Press, 1964. The book deals with attitudes, feelings, and beliefs about many aspects of college life, taken from interviews with students. It examines the student's thinking on the aims of education, curriculum, and teachers, his political and religious views, and on many aspects of life with which he is concerned. The book's aim is to explore the relationship between intellectual and emotional growth in the student. More suitable for upperclassmen.

RESNICK, WILLIAM C., AND DAVID H. HELLER (eds.): *On Your Own in College*. Columbus: Charles E. Merrill, 1962. An excellent collection of articles written by educators from various academic fields, presenting the typical social and academic difficulties of college beginners. The book contains advice and essential details of some useful notions for the better understanding of the meaning of education, college life, and the student's reaction to college. Written in pleasant and simple language, and primarily aimed at the college freshman, the articles introduce a variety of very useful research and study skills, and effective learning techniques. Contains a rich bibliography.

SANFORD, NEVITT: *College and Character*. New York: Wiley, 1964. A briefer and modified version of *The American College*, compiled by the same author. A collection of articles encompassing nearly all aspects of college life, problems of higher education, and the impact of the educational forces on the student. It examines the individual, social, and academic phases of higher education and how they are mutually affected. Appropriate for college students and the general reader.

SUTHERLAND, ROBERT L., et al. (ed.): *Personality Factors on the College Campus*. Austin: University of Texas Press, 1962. A symposium sponsored by the Hogg Foundation for Mental Health. It explores the influence of the educational objectives and of the student's peer groups on his personality growth. The book examines the role of the college curriculum and of the academic staff in meeting the student's emotional needs, and describes the levels of mental health among college students, with illustrations of appropriate case material. It also shows how students and subcultures in college are mutually affected. A very illuminating discussion beneficial to all class levels, and particularly to majors in educational psychology. Contains a rich bibliography.

TOWNSEND, AGATHA: *College Freshmen Speak Out*. New York: Harper, 1956. Contains the results of a questionnaire circulated among freshmen from various colleges, regarding their experience with problems deriving from their transition and adjustment to college. Their attitudes toward many aspects of college life are explored, and their reactions toward counselors and teachers are surveyed. Interesting reading for everyone.

VOEKS, VIRGINIA: *On Becoming an Educated Person*. Philadelphia: Saunders, 1957. Discusses the purpose of a college education and proposes the techniques for cultivating the proper personality attitudes to achieve it. The book offers direct advice, based on research, for developing desirable study habits and contains an excellent account for resolving difficulties with parents and for coping with feelings of dependency, hostility, and fear of failure in college. Excellent reading for all college levels.

WARTERS, JANE: *Achieving Maturity*. New York: McGraw-Hill, 1949. The author describes vividly the problems of adolescents, and discusses in a direct way the methods for personality improvement and for achieving responsibility and independence. She presents ways for resolving frustration and feelings of inferiority, and for achieving physical, social and mental adaptation to college. An excellent book for all college levels, and particularly for lowerclassmen.

WEDGE, BRYANT M. (ed.): *Psychosocial Problems of College Men*. New Haven: Yale University Press, 1958. Reports investigations by various authors of the personality development of the college student. It contains quantitative studies of achievement, competitiveness, methods and results of treatment, and understanding of the formation of the common emotional conflicts of college students. It attempts to explore emotional and social factors associated with the student's maladaptive behavior in college. A technical book written mainly for persons in the academic and mental health field. Upperclassmen and graduate students will also find the information useful.

WHITTINGTON, H. G.: *Psychiatry on the Campus.* New York: International Universities Press, 1963. The author describes the personality characteristics of students who seek psychological assistance and the methods used to identify the potentially disturbed college student. He discusses screening and treatment methods, furnishes illustrative case histories, outcome of treatment, follow-up studies, and proposes evaluations, recommendations, and methods for collecting valuable background data on each student. A worthwhile source for those interested in mental health research.

WISE, MAX: *They Came for the Best Reasons.* Washington, D. C.: American Council on Education, 1958. A brief account of the general trends in student behavior in college. It contains a statistical study of the academic and socio-economic status of the college population, and of students' attitudes toward outlook on life, adjustment to college, and toward social activities. Suitable reading for everyone.

ZWEIG, FERDYNAND: *The Student in the Age of Anxiety.* New York: Free Press, 1963. A study of English students from two British universities, surveying their opinions, interests, and some of the emotional problems affecting them. Their family backgrounds, social conditions, and the university atmosphere are examined. Proper for all readers.

✿　✿　✿　✿

# INDEX